# The Reading ]

*a link with the Anglo-Saxon Migration*

*Frontispiece*: A Lailey elm bowl in the collection of the Museum of English Rural Life at the University of Reading today. This bowl would have been sold as a 12in bowl. In fact, it measures a little over 11in in diameter. The reversed bowl pictured below has his signature which reads: *GW Lailey Dec 29 1937*.

# The Reading Lathe:
## *a link with the Anglo-Saxon Migration*

by

Philip H. Dixon

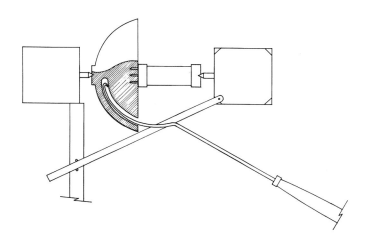

PUBLISHED BY CROSS PUBLISHING

NEWPORT, ISLE OF WIGHT

© Philip H. Dixon 1994
First Published 1994

Produced & Published by Cross Publishing,
Newport, Isle of Wight

British Library Cataloguing-in-Publication Data
A catalogue record for this book is
available from the British Library

ISBN 1 873295 65 0

# Contents

NOTES follow each chapter. Figures in brackets refer.

# List of Illustrations

Reading numbers to captions are the serial numbers of the Photograph Collection of the Rural History Centre at the University of Reading.

# Foreword

*by Dr EJT Collins, Rural History Centre, University of Reading*

One of the curious facts of English economic history is that so many of the traditional craft trades should not only have survived the upheaval of the Industrial Revolution but to have expanded, to reach their peak in terms of output and numbers employed in and around the mid-nineteenth century. Thereafter began the decline, at first gradual but from the 1880s precipitous to the point where, by the eve of the Great War, most branches of the old craft industry had all disappeared, extinguished by a combination of cheap imports, and changes in fashion and raw materials, and not least, factory competition.

When in 1920 Katherine Woods visited the woodland districts of Berkshire and Buckinghamshire during her survey of rural industries in the Oxford region, she was uniquely placed to record the products, methods of production and business organisation of what little remained of the old craft trades in this once important manufacturing centre. George William Lailey at Bucklebury Common was the only bowl turner then working in the region - and one of perhaps half a dozen in the whole of Britain - and, it was claimed, the only craftsman then actually using a traditional pole lathe. Much of what is known about this ancient tool and the pre-industrial art of bowl-turning is based on the record of work of the craftsman.

This study by Philip Dixon is an invaluable contributuion to industrial history. As he points out, bowl-turning was already obsolescent in Tudor times when pewter replaced wood in the better-off households. It declined in the seventeenth and eighteenth century due to the advent of cheap pottery and in the nineteenth to competition from galvanized iron. William and George Lailey owed their survival, and the latter his comfortable livelihood, to the Arts and Crafts movement, and the resultant demand by the middle classes for authentic craftsmen-made articles. Typically Lailey's bowls were sold by fashionable department stores such as Harrods and Heelas of Reading.

George Lailey was the last survivor, at least in southern England, of the once large numbers of wood-craftsmen who worked with pole-lathes. In the mid nineteenth century, there were perhaps several hundred in the Chiltern beechwoods turning chair legs, and many more on and around the sandy commons to the south of the river Kennet making broom handles and brush stocks. Up to the end of the century a few could still be found in many country towns, even in London. Bucklebury and the adjoining parishes had its own little nest of bowl-turners, perhaps three to four families, as likewise did Burnham in Buckinghamshire.

The original 'Lailey Lathe' and other tools, rescued fron the workshop at Bucklebury Common before it was demolished in 1959, survive in the University of Reading's Museum of English Rural Life, the centrepiece of a display of traditional woodworking crafts. The material is now complemented by this important study of the tool, the craftsmen who used it, and a technology which, in much of its original form survived from Anglo-Saxon times up to almost the present day.

# Acknowledgements

Thanks are due to Meg Cooper for the results of her genealogical research; to John Creasey, the Librarian of the Rural History Centre at the University of Reading for providing both a large quantity of documentation and for dealing with the photographs, both from Reading and elsewhere and for many useful references; to Cecilia Millson, the Berkshire rural historian for much matter from her files; and to Dr Helen Whitehouse of the Ashmolean Museum, Oxford, for the data used to describe the very earliest turning lathes.

One must not forget Godfrey Eke, a technician at the Rural History Centre (now retired) who not only provided many details of the work of the chair bodgers of the Chilterns (in which area he was brought up) but also carried out tests with mandrels on the Reading Lathe itself.

# Location of Turner's Green

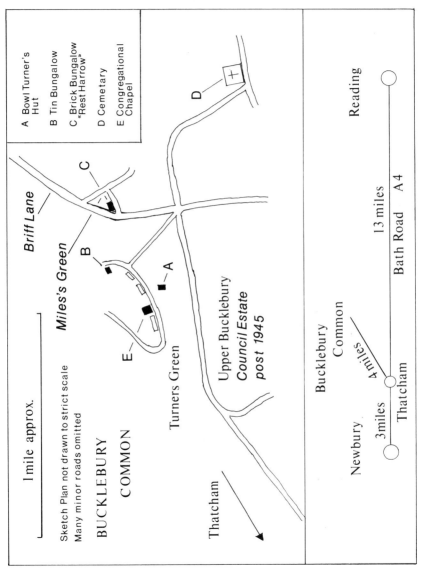

1 mile approx.

Sketch Plan not drawn to strict scale
Many minor roads omitted

BUCKLEBURY
COMMON

Briff Lane

Miles's Green

A Bowl Turner's Hut
B Tin Bungalow
C Brick Bungalow "Rest Harrow"
D Cemetary
E Congregational Chapel

Turners Green

Upper Bucklebury
Council Estate
post 1945

Thatcham

Newbury

3 miles

Thatcham

4 miles

Bucklebury
Common

13 miles

Bath Road    A4

Reading

# Chronological Table of the Lailey family

| Name | Born | Occupation | Died | Marr. | Wife's Name | Born | Died | Issue |
|---|---|---|---|---|---|---|---|---|
| James | 1746 (1) | Agr. Labourer | 1835 | 1768 | Mary Pauling | 1747 (1) | 1819 | (4) 11 children of whom William was 7th child and 4th son |
| William | 1782 (1) | Bowl Turner | 1871 | 1803 | 1. Elizabeth Ann Streatley | 1780 (1) | 1839 | 1 possible child traced |
| | | | | 1840 | 2. Elizabeth Wilshire | 1809 (2) | 1883 | 5 children of whom William was 4th child and 3rd son |
| William | 1847 | Bowl Turner | 1912 | 1869 | Kate Robbins | 1848 | 1921 (3) | 11 children of whom George Willam was 1st child |
| George William | 1869 | Bowl Turner | 1958 | - | Batchelor | | | |

NOTE: All wives were spinsters at marriage

*REVISED 24.5.88*

(1) Date inferred from age at burial
(2) Date from Census returns; differs from age at burial
(3) Entry untraced; date from contemporary sources
(4) Includes infant of under 1 year

## Chapter One

# The Bucklebury Bowl Turners

Prominently displayed in the Museum of English Rural Life, attached to the Institute of Agricultural History at Reading University, recently renamed the Rural History Centre, is a bowl turner's lathe. Acquired by the Museum in 1959, this remarkable machine was then more than 100 years old.

George William Lailey, the craftsman whose lathe it was, had died in the previous year, aged 89. He was the last bowl turner in England to follow the trade of hand-turned wooden bowl making as a living. He had never married and with him there ended a line of tradesmen whose family is recorded as far back as the middle of the eighteenth century. All his life, he had worked in the one place, a hut at Turner's Green on Bucklebury Common in Berkshire.

Wooden bowls and platters were used by all classes for domestic purposes from Anglo-Saxon times until their first decline with the advent of pewter in the Tudor period and earlier. Thereafter, the use of wood for household ware dwindled. The process was accelerated by the plentiful supply of cheap crockery and glass, available from *c* 1750 onwards. Later, tinplate and enamel-ware reduced the demand still further. Wooden bowl and platter turning became a woodland industry, surviving for the most part in the remoter districts of Pembrokeshire and the Welsh Marches, and also in certain English rural areas, part icularly in Berkshire, Shropshire and Northamptonshire. Many parts of the country remained in comparative isolation long after the building of the railways, but before the general arrival of the motorbus and the motorcar. In the mid-nineteenth century, when most of the rail network had already been built, regular connection to the outside world was maintained by the postman and the weekly carrier's cart.

Until the beginning of the present century, wooden bowls, tubs and churns were still used in dairies and farm kitchens, but these were mostly the cooper's rather than the turner's products. Until quite recently, wood was the normal material for barrel spigots, round clothes pegs, cooking spoons and the like, but these had long been made by automatic lathes and special machinery. Certain ancient institutions, Winchester School for example, used wooden platters for meat until a very late date. The newly founded Reading University is said to have so equipped its dining hall in the twenties. Such is the power of tradition.

As will be seen from the Chronological Table, the Lailey family has been traced back to James Lailey (?1746-1835), described as 'Agricultural Labourer', who was the father of William Lailey (1782-1871), the first of the Laileys to be recorded as 'Bowl Turner'. It was he who built the sunken-floored workshop at Turner's Green on Bucklebury Common. If the Bucklebury Manor Rolls have been correctly interpreted, this hut was erected in 1826, or just before.

This William was George William Lailey, the last bowl turner's grandfather, who (assuming the 1826 date to be correct) was then 44 years old. After his death in 1871 his son, also William (b 1847) continued the business until he in turn died in 1912. George William (b 1869) carried on alone (so far as the actual turning was concerned) until his death in December, 1958, aged 89 years.

When the first William Lailey, who must already have been a practised bowl turner (1), started his business on the Common his products were sold for their workaday value alone. He and his successors used only elm wood as raw material. His two lathes could also be used to make longer, cylindrical objects such as candleholders, balusters and tool handles as well as bowls. It is not thought that such turnery formed more than a small part of his output. Later, the second William (Figure 1) would sometimes make breadboards. Bowls were always the principal product and there is no evidence that his son George William (Figure 2) ever turned any long pieces. Bowls and ladles (or handled bowls, which were his speciality), and an occasional breadboard were his, George William's, sole products.

Many woodland turners were working in the Kennet Valley prior to 1914. Some were on Bucklebury Common and others made up a small colony at Mortimer, on the opposite side of the river. None is recorded as a bowl turner. Only two of these were still in business after 1918: Jim West, on the Common, made implement handles and the like (ceased c 1940); Albert Carter (Figure 17), at Stoke Row, turned chair legs and other furniture parts, mostly for repairs and replacements (ceased c 1939). Both these used chair bodger's lathes, a lighter type of machine which is described later.

During the nineteenth century, various craft movements followed the emergence of William Morris (1834-96) and the founding of the Kelmscott Press. He was himself a great designer of fabrics and wallpapers, works of high art which are reproduced to this day in both materials. His dictum that, 'the true incentive to useful and happy labour is, and must be,

1. William Lailey (GW Lailey's father) stands outside the bowl turner's hut on Bucklebury Common, *c* 1900 (perhaps 1898). He is preparing a bowl blank. A completed hemisphere stands at the foot of the chopping block. Behind him is a stack of elm logs. Through the open door is a glimpse of the window in the N wall which lighted the ground level part of the hut. It was kept shuttered after 1918, when work was no longer done there, and was boarded over during the re-cladding of *c* 1938. William is in his fifties. *Reading 5/230.*

2. George William Lailey finishing a ladle, *c* 1908. He is in his late thirties and is using a spokeshave. The stop fitted to the shaving horse is recessed to accept the end of the handle. The stack of logs, seen in Figure 1 has been used and new stock is elsewhere. *Reading 5/231.*

pleasure in the work itself' reflects a growing desire of the time to own and use handmade things which has persisted to the present day. Underlying it was the idea that a nation of craftsmen would be happier than one devoted to making things in factories.

The essence of mass production is a uniformity of product and of the means of making it. This enables the various operations necessary to complete it to be divided between specialised groups of workers or machines. Add to this the use of power in place of physical labour and you have the essence of the Industrial Revolution. Its potency lies in the reduction achieved in the cost of each article. This permits larger quantities to be sold at lower cost to an increasing market: distributed by the new railway network, prices were kept low at point of sale.

A reaction against mass produced domestic objects commenced during the second half of the nineteenth century. At this time, factory processes had as yet hardly touched a large number of trades and crafts, especially rural ones, although the generality of domestic requirements from cloth to washing bowls, from cutlery to fire irons, was already factory made. This development revitalized the Lailey's business. A preference for wooden artefacts steadily developed. Wood is pleasant to handle and the grain can be good to look at. The trend reached its apogee in the early 1900s when Bucklebury-turned bowls became normal stock at Harrods. The then largest bowls had a high utilitarian value: their use was reserved for the washing of silver and fine porcelain. At that time the Lailey's did not turn anything bigger than 15in (38cm) diameter. The smaller sizes, down to 6in (15cm) diameter, were in demand as fruit bowls, salad bowls and for bread rolls, followed by use as collectors of small objects, bunches of keys and even soap. At least one Bond Street perfumier sold three tablets of soap packed in a Lailey 6in bowl.

The advantage and convenience of wooden bowls for various purposes is easily seen and the pleasure of handling them likewise. As a fruit holder, for example, a wooden bowl is completely in harmony with its contents. The question must here be asked, why did Harrods department store, with a good trade going, not then commission some turnery with large power-driven lathes to run off a suitable quantity of bowls as required? The answer to this is in two parts. First, and more important, comes the use of the magic words 'Hand Made'. Clearly there is no utilitarian gain from a hand-turned object as against a machine made one. The fact that no two of the Lailey bowls were exactly alike could have been of no moment in terms of use. The pleasure felt in handling and owning such a craftsman's product lies in the association between a natural material and another human being. This aesthetic is entirely lost when factory production intervenes. In short, we feel something of the corollary of William Morris's perception: we are affected by the notion that the worker who made our product was happy in so doing: that is, he put something of himself into it. In addition, we know that every handmade thing is unique and that we thus own what no one else does. But Lailey's bowls always had a high utilitarian content. These were pre-plastic days.

The second part of the answer is wholly on a material plane. The Lailey's had no overheads. Even the minute sums levied by the Court Baron in former times were no longer collected. As shown later, the cost of their elm wood was but a fraction of their charge for a finished bowl. Thus the selling price, less a small sum for material and an even smaller one for the labour to cut it into billets, was profit. Living in the country, within easy walking distance of the their work, father and son enjoyed a very adequate yield. But at this level, no manufactory could ever match their prices and have a margin. Only if the quantities required had risen from dozens to thousands would factory production have stood a chance.

The surge of business experienced by the Laileys in the 1900s was at the high tide of the William Morris craftwork movement. This was the time of Art Nouveau, the Liberty period and of the founding of the first Garden City, (Letchworth, 1903). Orders for the wooden bowls came from many other large department stores besides Harrods (2). It was probably from Harrods that a request came for a larger size of bowl in which to wash the silverware and the porcelain. To meet this demand, the centre height of one lathe had to be raised to accommodate an 18in (45cm) diameter bowl. From this time on, this lathe (which is the Reading Lathe) became known as the 'large bowl lathe' and the other, unmodified, was the 'small bowl lathe'. It is thought that George William turned all the large diameter bowls on the former lathe and that his father (then nearly 60 years old) prepared all the turning blanks and turned the smaller bowls on the other lathe.

The raising of the centres enabled ladles (or handled bowls) to be turned; a thing which would have been impossible with the old centre height. These ladles were said to have been sold for emptying kitchen clothes-boiling coppers, which were very common in those days (3). For this purpose, they would have been exceedingly clumsy and inefficient compared to the ordinary galvanized iron dippers, factory made, cheap and stocked by every ironmonger, and costing no more than one fifth of the price of a wooden ladle. But they were much safer to use inside a copper cauldron. It seems possible that they were developed to a specific request and afterwards sold for other purposes (as described below).

George Lailey's father died in 1912. This was the close of a golden era for the Bucklebury business. During the whole period from its foundation until 1914, the Laileys had used casual or itinerant labour to cut up the elm logs, stacked in the open to season. When the hut was reclad in corrugated iron sheeting (c 1870, or perhaps a little before), a lean-to was added on the east side. In this were stacked the cut and split half-round billets from which the turning blanks were later prepared. Knowing George William's best weekly output of bowls, it can be calculated that, with him and his father working together, about 1000 billets would have made up a half year's supply. This quantity could have been sawn, split and stacked in the shed by two good labourers working for a couple of weeks or so. The time saved by the Laileys in having this rough work done, and doubtless paid for at the lowest going agricultural wage (4), was translated into additional turning time, and thus money, at a profitable rate. When production was at its peak in the 1900s, such men may have been more often employed, doing everything except the final preparation of the blanks into hemispheres and the actual turning.

Within two years of George William's father's death, the First World War broke out. An early consequence was that all the casual labour disappeared. Lailey, who had been continuing the business as the sole turner since 1912, now recruited his mother to work with him in the cross-sawing of the elm logs into billets (5), he then being 45 and she 66 years old. Except for some help from an octogenarian (as will be described later) in the thirties, Lailey worked entirely alone at his bowl and ladle making until his death in 1958, a period of some 47 years.

War having started, two developments occurred, both favourable to the business.

Lailey soon received large orders (large by his standards, that is) for the wooden ladles which he had first made in the 1900s. These were required for use in gunpowder handling in munition works in place of the normal copper ladles. This metal had very quickly become in short supply, being used in large quantity for the driving bands of shells. In 1914, the majority of shells used by the Royal Navy, and all of those used by the army, were still gunpowder filled (common shell). It was not until the time of the Somme (1916) that British artillery in France was supplied with high explosive filled shells (HE). By then, all shell production had become high explosive filled, but large quantities of gunpowder were still used for minor weaponry, signalling rockets, Very lights and pyrotechnics of all kinds.

These wooden ladles were slow to make. With Lailey having to perform all operations from the cut billet to the finished article, it is estimated that the output cannot much have exceeded one-and-a-half completed ladles per working day. The initial order for ladles for wartime use is thought to have been for 20 dozen (240) items. This would have represented nearly half a year's work, assuming that he made no bowls in the same period. A secondary effect of this slow rate would have been to reduce the workload on the old lady, there being many fewer billets needed.

The second development brought about by wartime was the rapidly increasing shortage of tinned and enamel ware for domestic use. Almost overnight, 100 years of change in the bowl maker's market, from an entirely practical product to a largely *recherché* craft article was reversed.

Regardless of their greater cost, wooden bowls became essential substitutes for unobtainable metal goods. Until well after the end of the war in 1918, Lailey was in arrears with his deliveries.

By the early twenties, the basis of demand had moved back again in character to that of the beginning of the century. It was now that bowls, signed and dated on the base by the bowlmaker, became prized possessions. *(See frontispiece)*. They were even given as wedding presents. Articles began to appear in local newspapers (6), in *The Times*, in glossy magazines such as *Country Life*, and an account of the Bucklebury bowl-turner formed the first chapter of HV Morton's *In Search of England* (1927).

As noted above, sometime in the 1900s the Laileys had been obliged to alter one of their lathes by raising the centres to accommodate the turning of 18in (45cm) diameter bowls. Shortly after the end of the war (1922 is a probable date) Lailey received a request from the Royal Mint for an even larger bowl, one of 20in (50cm) diameter, to hold quantities of newly struck coins. Then in his early fifties, he successfully made about 100 of these. As will be seen when the turning processes on a pole lathe are described, this entailed very heavy work indeed. This was the last entirely practical and purely commercial assignment which he ever undertook. As far as is known, he never turned this size again, although he made 18in (45cm) diameter bowls up to the last war (1939) and was turning 12in (30cm) diameter bowls until the year he died (1958). It was claimed by a writer in *Country Life* in 1945 that 24in (60cm) diameter bowls had formerly been made. There is no written confirmation of this, though possibly such a bowl appears in one photograph. This size of bowl was within the capacity of the lathe which then had a swing of $13^1/_2$in (34cm) over the bed, but the labour involved would have been immense, due to the weight of the necessary blank and its consequent inertia. However, the largest bowl in Figure 3 may be a 24in one. This was clearly an exhibition set. Hence the absence of any evidence that such bowls were normally made and sold. The date of the photograph may be 1921. Lailey would then have been about 53 years old. It is just possible that accounts have been muddled and that this was indeed the size for the Royal Mint.

When the previous war ended (1918), Lailey's mother could no longer assist him with the cross-sawing of timber, she then being 70 years old. The answer to this problem was to buy the elm ready cut into half rounds from the sawmill of Barlow & Sons at Hermitage, Berkshire. This material was delivered to the hut on Bucklebury Common by lorry. No timber which had not been airdried for less than four years was ever used.

3. George William Lailey showing a set of bowls, *c* 1922.
The largest bowl *may* be 24in diameter. The roof of handmade tiles, put on *c* 1912, shows some deterioration. The half-doors are now hung to the RH door stile. The weatherboard cladding, presumed to have been applied when the new roof was done, has suffered severely. Only the gable and the upper part on the W side remains more or less intact. The remainder has been made good with odd boards and large areas of corrugated iron sheet, doubtless saved from the 1912 work. The timber to the R, partly in front of door of the E side lean-to, consists of butt ends from stocks of logs cut up prior to 1918, when the use of ready-cut material was adopted. Lailey is in his early fifties. Note also that what had been open Common in the background to the N has now feen fenced off by the new owners of plots from the break- up of the manorial estate in 1921. *Reading 35/4485.*

After his father's death in 1912, the output of the business must have dropped to about half. This would have caused the stock of logs, drying in piles around the hut, to diminish much more slowly than before. It seems certain that the stock in hand in 1914, combined with the relatively slow usage occasioned by the ladle making, enabled the pre-war stocks, with little or no addition, to outlast the 1914-18 period. Demand for elm (as opposed, e.g., to softwoods) had not been particularly high during the war, and Barlows would have had plenty of wood, seasoned for four or five years, in their extensive yards. Lailey would always have known the seasoning time of material sent to him and rarely, if ever, used the blocks on receipt, but kept them stacked outside or in the lean-to for another year or so. In its cut up form, this timber would airdry very rapidly.

In Figure 1, (c 1900), a stack of uncut logs may be seen in the background. In Figure 3 (early 1920s), when ready-cut and split wood had already been used for some time, the butts of pre-1914 logs are piled to the right of the hut. Figure 4, (taken a few years later) shows some of the stock of cut timber. Such material may also be seen in Figure 5, (c 1938). No later photograph includes any timber outside the hut and there is written evidence that none was to be seen after c 1942(8). As the turner had no assistance, it is probable that the sawmill collected the older knarled remains, cut from them what was usable, and returned the salvaged pieces to the lean-to.

George William Lailey was born in 1869 at a cottage in Miles Green, about a mile to the northeast of Turner's Green. This dwelling was part of the Bucklebury manorial estate. As far as is known, his grandfather, still alive at this date, also lived there. The Laileys then had Common rights. These comprised the grazing of cattle on the Common, sheep in summer, the gathering of firewood and the cutting of fern after September 1st. There was no right to erect buildings on the Common, but many did

4. Two unknown women with bowls outside the hut c 1924: another is entering the lean-to from the S through its only door . The timber stock at R is now of ready-cut pieces. The cladding has deteriorated still further and even the small window has lost some of its glazing bars. Before 1930, as photographs then taken show, this was replaced by one with a 12-light cast iron frame which survived the hut's life. *Reading 35/13514.*

so and were annually fined for the encroachment by the Court Baron held for the Lord of the Manor by his steward.

Some relevant entries (9) for William Lailey (the grandfather) were:

| | |
|---|---|
| 1820 pigsties, carthouse & woodhouse | $1\frac{1}{2}$d |
| 1826 workshop and carthouse | $1\frac{3}{4}$d |
| additional amercement | 3s 6d |
| 1834 carthouse | 1d |
| workshop | $3\frac{1}{2}$d |
| 1872 workshop (per Elizabeth Lailey, his widow) | $3\frac{1}{2}$d |

(For these sums in decimal coinage, see Table V)

The special fine of 3/6d in 1826 (which was 12 times the subsequent annual charge - itself doubled from previous years) was almost certainly levied because Lailey had dug a pit in which to erect his workshop. Buildings on the Common, the subject of these fines, were supposed to be only of a temporary nature. Digging a pit and erecting six massive vertical members for a strong hut was something far beyond pigsties or a shelter for a cart.

After his father died in 1912, George William remained at the Miles Green cottage, his mother acting as housekeeper until her death in 1921. In that year, a large part of the manorial estate was put on the market (10). The cottage was auctioned and he was unable (or unwilling) to outbid the sale figure reached. Instead, he bought himself a plot of land in Long Grove, within the parish of Bucklebury, and had built a corrugated iron bungalow of a type which often appeared during the early inter-war period, Government surplus material and, in form, not unlike the more recent 'pre-fabs'. Here he lived for the next twenty five years, with a sister and successive nieces keeping house for him. (See Appendix A for one of the Lailey myths).

As soon as he left the house in Miles Green, Lailey lost his Common rights and his workshop technically made him a trespasser at Turner's Green (11). With the break-up of the estate in 1921, no one seems to have bothered very much. At this time, the manorial rights over the Common passed to the Berkshire County Council. In conversation, he would claim that he still had his rights as he still lived within the parish, but legally he had none.

Finally, in 1939, he bought a plot in Briff Lane, Bucklebury, from the then Lord of the Manor with a view to building himself a house. The last war having intervened, he was unable to do this until 1946. Here he lived, going to the hut when he felt like it, and refusing more orders than he actually turned. From first to last, the workshop had no heating or lighting or power: other that is, than from the hotbed of shavings upon which he stood; daylight, and a hurricane lamp for emergencies only: and the power of his own left leg.

Figure 1 is the earliest picture of the hut extant. It is assigned to *c* 1900, but the exact date may be a little before that, say 1898. It shows George William's father who would then have been 51 years old. He is trimming an elm block to form a set of bowls from 15in (38cm) dia downwards, as will be described in the next chapter. He is using an ordinary chopper of the sort sold everywhere for splitting kindling sticks (12). A completed blank may be seen at the foot of the chopping block.

The hut is clad in and roofed with corrugated iron sheets. This material came into general use *c* 1870, or a little before. The original hut, as built in 1826, was probably of either riven or pit-sawn boards, which may have been of elm if they lasted for the 50 years until the iron sheets became available. The roof may have been thatched.

Figure 2 was taken *c* 1908 and shows George William, aged about 39, finishing one of his ladles, using a shaving horse (13). The roof and cladding remain the same and the tree in the distance has put on about 10 years of growth.

After his father's death in 1912, Lailey had a new roof built on the hut. The next available photographs, Figures 3 and 4, date from 10 to 12 years later. The tiled roof is not doing too badly (it was to last for another 45 years) but the cladding is clearly in a bad way. It is assumed that when the roof was rebuilt using handmade tiles, the intention was to remake the walls in weatherboard. Perhaps the onset of the war prevented this being completed, or executed in a satisfactory manner. Whatever the reason, large areas were again covered in corrugated iron sheets, doubtless recovered from the old cladding. This state of affairs lasted until *c* 1938, when the workshop was again reclad in weatherboard as may be seen in Figures 5 and 6, the roof remaining untouched. Figures 7 and 8 show the basic structural features of the hut. In the late 1940s there was a near disaster as the tie beam (probably newly inserted when the tiled roof was put on *c* 1912) had rotted away and parted company with the massive central upright on the east side as indicated. It did not fall down as it was

5. Lailey displaying 18in (34cm) diameter bowls, c 1937. The hut has at last been re-clad in weatherboard and has new half-doors and shutters. The roof remains unaltered and its state appears somewhat better than as seen in Figures 3 and 4, a number of tiles having been replaced. Note the pile of half-round billets from the sawmill. Lailey is about 68 years old. *Reading 35/26104.*

6. Lailey in 1939, now turned 70 years of age, with Rose Iremonger, a local child. The cladding of the hut seems to be in excellent condition. Note the band round Lailey's left leg (his treadling leg) below the knee, to lift his trouser leg from his boot and to keep out the shavings, dust and chips from the turning process. *Reading 35/27432.*

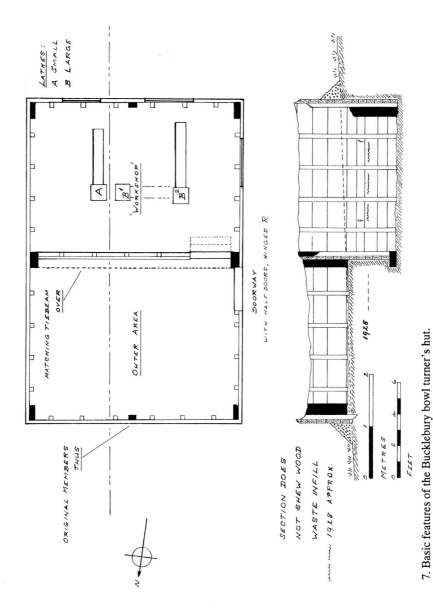

LATHES:
A SMALL
B LARGE

MATCHING TIEBEAM OVER

ORIGINAL MEMBERS THUS

'WORKSHOP'

A

B¹

B²

OUTER AREA

DOORWAY
WITH HALF DOORS, HINGED R

SECTION DOES
NOT SHEW WOOD
WASTE INFILL
~~~~ 1928 APPROX.

N

1928

METRES
0    1    2    3

FEET
0    2    4    6

7. Basic features of the Bucklebury bowl turner's hut.
A. is a plan view with *approximate* lathe positions. A and B1 are earlier and B2 is post *c* 1930 after the headstock had rotted away in the shavings hotbed.

25

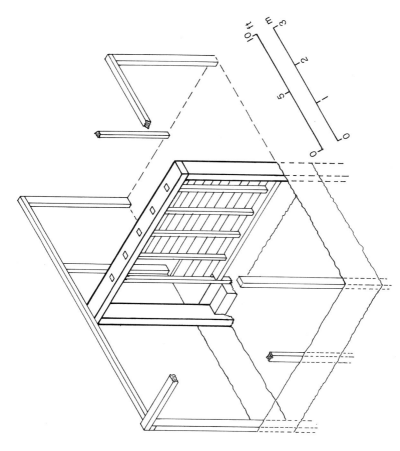

7B. The pit, with two steps down, is as it was c 1927. The partition runs E-W and the 'large bowl lathe' at this time also stood with its axis E - W. The turner worked with his back to the partition (see also Figure 28). The 'small bowl lathe', unused after 1918, stood at right-angles to it.

10 ft

m 3

2

5

0

0

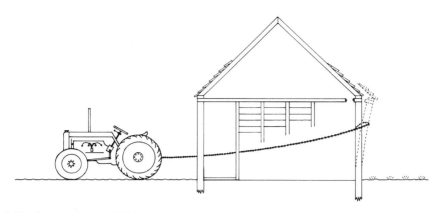

8. The hut repair, post 1945.
When the tiebeam rotted through as shown, the weight of the tiled roof was taken via a king-post (not drawn) by the partition which bowed somewhat and allowed the central upright, opposite the doorway, to be pushed outwards. By jacking up the wall plates centrally, the old tiebeam and the entire partition was removed and not replaced. The removed tiebeam is seen in Figure 9 and seems to have been a common deal beam, inserted when the new tiled roof went on c 1912.

supported by the central partition. The downthrust from the several tons of tiled roof pushed out the post and the entire weight was effectively taken by the partition.

This highly dangerous condition caused Lailey's many friends to fear for the old man's life when strong winds swept the Common (14 ). The remedy was to fit a new tiebeam. To do this, a tractor and chains, brought by a neighbouring farmer, was used to pull the bend out of the central post as shown and to fit a new tiebeam. This entailed removing the partition which was not replaced. The old tiebeam, with the mortices for the studs of the partition, may be seen in Figure 9 which is of the interior and the north wall, a photograph taken by the Museum in early 1959, shortly before the removal of the lathe and the demolition of the hut. Figure 10 is a final view of the exterior as it then was.

The six main and two subsidiary posts do not come out very clearly in any of the photographs taken in 1959. But they were carefully measured and described by the Reading technicians, and so recorded. All were of riven oak and there is every probability that (except for the tiebeam) all were the original members, erected in 1826, and still standing squarely to the end.

The form of the workshop proper was that of the sunken-floored huts

9. The interior of the N (ground level) part of the hut in 1959. The old tiebeam leans against the new one. The mortices for the studs of the original partition show clearly. The blackening of the end which rests on the ground probably connotes rot. The lathe pole, which formerly passed over and rested upon, the tiebeam, is now secured to a door stile in the crudest 'make-do' manner. The earlier anchorage would have been a post in the floor about at the T-shaped sunbeam reflection. *Reading 5/429.*

10. A last view of the hut from the NW. The wall to R with patching sheet of corrugated iron was irretrievably damaged by the main lathe being secured to it after c 1930 when the foot of the headstock had rotted away, due to having been sunk into a hotbed of wood chippings and shavings for a century. The damage to the wall was the result of nearly 30 years of vibration from the lathe. *Reading 5/433.*

or *grubenhäuser* first introduced into England by the fifth centry Anglo-Saxon immigrants. Many hundreds of these huts have been excavated. With these people also came the turning of wooden cups and bowls on pole lathes for general domestic use. The Coppergate, York, excavations have revealed the remains of bowl turning activities in close association with sunken-floored workshops (dated *c* 900) which are comparable with Lailey's (15). A few other sites where there was either sterile soil (as at York), or wet conditions such as the bottom of a well , have also yielded parts of bowls dating from Anglo-Saxon times. Dr Carole Morris, Cambridge, is the authority for their analysis. The building of the Bucklebury hut with a sunken floor was the end of a long tradition, just as the form of the Reading lathe itself will be seen to derive: a persistence of design over fifteen centuries. As to the lathe itself, we also have a connecting link through a 13th century machine as will be seen later.

With Lailey's death in 1958 there ended a trade established in England in Anglo-Saxon times and obsolescent in Tudor times: carried out in a workshop similar in design to those known to have been in use in England from the 5th century: and pursued, using machines already out-of-date when they were first built (16). Excepting wear and tear and the rebuilding of the hut from time to time, four generations of Laileys had followed their ancient practices with the same equipment, on the same site and with no concessions whatever to modern times, for 130 years.

The lathe itself, focal to this continuum, will be described in its own place in the history of turning, a short account of which now follows.

# NOTES on Chapter One

1. Myres and Dixon, p 116 and Note 6. James Lailey was almost certainly a bowl turner. 'Agricultural labourer' was a general term used for rural workers. Similarly, his son was so called by the Census enumerators later on.

2. Woods, p 112.

3. Millson, p 58.

4. idem, p 59. The pay is believed to have been 6d per hour (see Table V, p 83), a fair pre-1914 rate. (There would have been no deductions before *c* 1908, if then. Each man would have received a sovereign (gold) and two florins (silver) for each 48 hours work).

5. Woods, p 112.

6. All newspaper articles and accounts in magazines are listed in the Bibiliography under *Ephemera*.

7. Millson, p 59, et al.

8. Millson, private correspondence.

9. Humphreys, p 371, et seq.

10. Julyan, et al.

11. Millson, private correspondence.

12. By contrast, G.W. Lailey, always used a 7 lb handaxe.

13. He is cleaning up that part of the circumference of the bowl's exterior which is level with the handle. For the handle itself, he used a drawknife.

14. Millson, op. cit. and private corespondence.

15. Hall, p 78.

16. Myres and Dixon, p 118, wrongly states 1880 as the probable date of building of the Bucklebury lathes: this should have read *c* 1830. This article lists the evidence for the sunken-floor feature which was not to be seen in 1959 as the pit was by now completely filled by the detritus of 130 years of bowl turning.

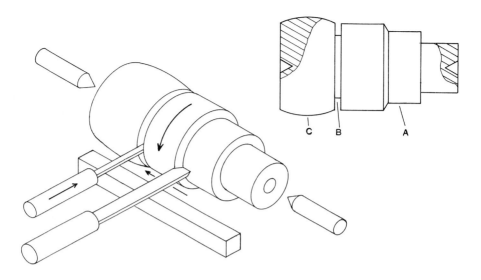

11. Cylindrical turning on any lathe.
A. Plain turning.  B. A plunge cut.  C. Form turning.

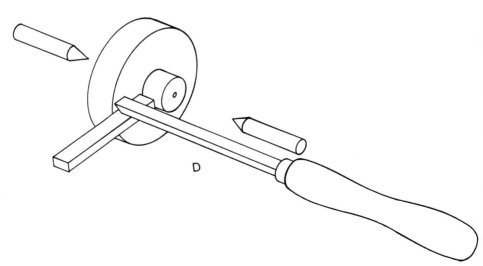

12. Face turning on any lathe, D.

*Chapter Two*

# Turning on Reciprocating Lathes

The basic wood turning process is shown in Figures 11 and 12. A length of any machinable material, preferably of roughly circular section, is mounted between pivots or centres and rotated in the direction shown. Parallel to this workpiece is a bearing bar or toolrest. A cutting tool of chisel-like form is held on the toolrest and pressed against the rotating material. The tool will then remove some of the workpiece in the form of chippings or shavings and leave a relatively smooth cylinder as at A, or will form a groove as at B. By combining these two motions, a curved shape may be formed as at C.

If an object of disc-like form is required, Figure 12 indicates how this can be done. A flat piece of material is mounted between the centres and its edge is first turned as at A. The toolrest and the tool are now transferred to position D and a cut is made across the axis of rotation. As before, grooves may be cut or a curved surface produced as the turner desires.

These simple procedures are labelled with their generally used terms, plain turning, face turning, plunge cutting. They have not altered in principle from the half-millennium BC to the present day. Most of the history of turning from its beginnings to the development of the screwcutting and automatic lathe by Maudslay (1771-1831) is concerned solely with the means by which the workpiece is rotated and the tool applied.

The earliest known representation of the turning process comes from Ptolemaic Egypt, *c* 300 BC and Figure 13 is a drawing of this. The turner squats with his cutting tool held against a vertical toolrest. The workpiece is rotated by an assistant (1) who holds the two ends of a strap with which he imparts a to-and-fro motion to the work. The turner would have used a rhythmic action in consonance with the manual power source: he would have moved his chisel slightly inwards across the tool rest for the cutting half of rotation and slightly outwards during the return half. Thus, work took place during only one half of his assistant's drive.

This type of lathe survived until quite recently and was to be seen in almost any *souq* from Morocco to the Gulf, wherever there was an area set apart for the makers of small artefacts. Some may still be in use.

Such lathes are, however, of the normal horizontal plan, as in Figures 11 and 12. Why then did the ancient artist present us with a nearly

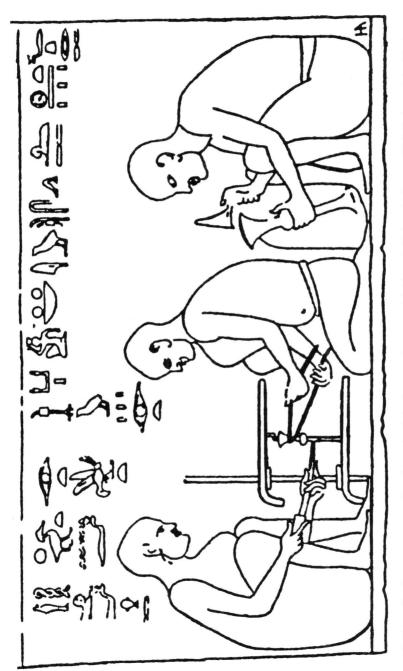

13. The earliest known representation of a turning lathe. It comes from a tomb in Egypt in Ptolemaic times, c 300 BC. As explained in the text, it is a plan view turned upright. The hieroglyphs on the left read: 'It is useful for the worker to do the work. His master will repay him for it'. Those on the right say: 'Craftsmen working without pause to serve their master, whose interests are in their hands'. Translations by Dr Helen Whitehouse, Ashmolean Museum, Oxford. After G Lefebure, *Le tombeau de Petosiris*, Paris, 1923.

impractical machine? The following comment was lately made by Dr Helen Whitehouse of the Ashmolean Museum at Oxford:

"The tomb is exceptionally interesting because its decoration (painted relief) combines both traditional Egyptian and "new" Greek elements, several of the latter to do with technical procedures. That does not necessarily mean that these things had come in with the Greek settlers, only that the Egyptians had for once been moved to step outside the conventions of Egyptian art, which was highly conservative and selective in what was shown". (Personal communication).

Now it is a matter of common observation that these artists had no tradition of perspective, nor of projection. There are two ways of providing a picture of such a lathe. The first is by the method of mechanical drawing. This would involve a plan view and one or more elevations and would hardly have been suitable for the artistic decoration of a tomb. The second way is by using some form of projection, such as the isometric which has been used in Figures 11 and 12; but this was unknown to the Egyptian artists. As no simple end view of this lathe would produce what the artist selectively saw, he overcame the difficulty by depicting the turner and his man in the usual flat (side elevation) manner, but rotated the plan view of the lathe itself into a vertical position. (As Dr Whitehouse has pointed out, this sort of thing was also done when a box and its contents were to be displayed). So, to understand what is shown, we have to imagine the whole machine turned back until it is horizontal (when we would then have an end view). Since the first essential was to delineate the turner and the lathe driver, which convention decreed could only be done on the flat, and an end view of the lathe would have been meaningless, an excellent plan (stripped to essentials) was shown in elevation.

The turning process will always leave a series of spiral grooves along the length of a machined cylinder, or across the face of a disc. The more slowly the tool is traversed, the finer the grooves. If a plunge cut is applied, that is one without any side movement of the cutting tool, the result will be a true circle. If a rotating turnpiece is smoothed by abrasion, the fine marks of the grit still have the same recognisable form under magnification. Using these criteria, Petrie (1853-1942) was unable to identify any turned objects among the very large number of cylindrical artefacts from earlier times in Egypt (2). However, Davies (in 1913) noted a fragment of a chair leg which still showed the cone-shaped hole of a centre of rotation at one end, though the workman's marks in the wood were not radial but at various angles. The whole problem was

14. Turnpiece from a proto-lathe.
This comes from Thebes in the Amarna period. The workman would have rotated his work with one hand and applied the tool with the other. See Figure 15. *After Manuelian.*

re-examined by Wainwright (in 1925) and he decided that such artefacts were first roughed out and then mounted between centres for finishing. He used the term 'proto-lathe' for the arrangement employed. This view was confirmed by Manuelian (in 1980) who pointed out that where rings had been cut with a vee-shaped chisel they wandered from a true circle, and that this is consistent with Wainwright's idea of the workpiece being rotated by one hand of the turner whilst his other applied the chisel (Figure 14). This was as near as the Egyptians came to true turning for about a thousand years before the arrival of the Greeks and Macedonians and the first real lathes.

Gordon Childe (1892-1957) (3), applying similar canons to those of Petrie, believed (but admitted that he could not prove) that such lathes were in use in Mesopotamia before the Greeks had them. On his evidence, these may have been proto-lathes.

Figure 15, from the Middle ages, has a paternosterer's lathe for the making of rosary beads. This device has neither pole nor treadle and the workpiece is driven by a bow and thong arrangement in the turner's right hand which imparts a reciprocating motion to the workpiece. In his left is what looks very like a hacksaw and he is clearly cutting the stem connecting each bead with the next. After form turning, the whole workpiece could then be broken up into individual spheres which would subsequently be drilled for threading. This machine is really a proto-lathe. With such light work it was not felt necessary to provide a pole and a treadle.

For heavier work, a pole lathe is essential. There has been much misconception about how such machines work.

Figure 16 shows schematically the action of a pole lathe. The following points should be noted:

First, the power delivered by a man's leg via a treadle is many times that available from a pair of hands pulling on a leather strap, whether in ancient Egypt or in a *souq* today. This power is again multiplied several times when the operator stands up to do his work, a thing not necessary

15. A mediaeval rosary - bead maker.
This is clearly a proto-lathe. The device in the turner's right hand imparts reciprocal rotation. In his left hand is the tool. This would have been of a different type to form the heads into spheres. This must be the first operation, spacing out the beads, but being careful not to leave the stem too weak. *After Stadbibl. Nurnberg MS Mendel Brunderbuch I. Amb. 317 fol.18v, 1405.*

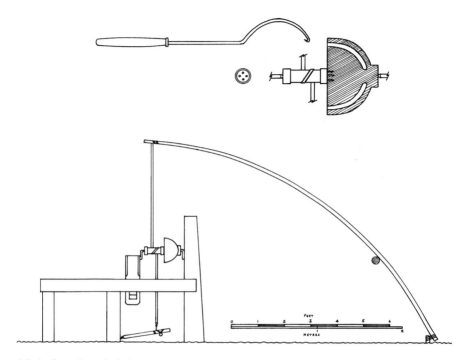

16. Action of a pole lathe.
This is schematic. This view is facing the turner. A bowl blank has been outside turned and is now ready for inside forming as shown at top. The essential tool rest is on the turner's (opposite) side and is not shown. In the case of the Bucklebury lathes, the poles rested on the tiebeam and their anchorages were in the north half of the hut (Figure 7). The springy pole holds the treadle in a raised position. When depressed by his foot the belt rotates the mandrel and turn-piece toward him and his cutting tool is advanced. The effort available for shearing off the wood is the turner's weight, delivered via his leg, *LESS* the tension imposed by the springy pole.

for turning chair legs or similar workpieces of small diameter.

Secondly, these aspects of the pole lathe, besides doing away with the second worker, also provide the means by which very much heavier workpieces can be machined. But the lost time and energy resulting from the reciprocating motion remain and are of greater consequence the greater the diameter and weight of the workpiece. We will return to this point later.

Thirdly, there has been some misunderstanding of the purpose of the sapling used with pole lathes. Several writers (4), including eminent ones, have referred to this feature or a similar one as the source of the power which drives the machine. In fact, depressing the pole during the down- or cutting-stroke *reduces* the energy available for cutting by a marginal amount. The power applied is that of the turner's left leg backed by his weight, *less* the effort in bending the pole.

To make this point quite clear:

When the turner thrusts down on his treadle, he causes the workpiece to revolve downwards towards him. His chisel or other cutting tool is advanced a little from its 'ready' position (just clear of the workpiece) and cutting occurs until the treadle reaches the floor (or other limit to its stroke). He then retracts slightly his cutting tool and lifts his foot, whereupon the workpiece revolves in the contra direction and the treadle rises again, impelled by the release of the tension imposed upon the spring, that is the sapling which acts as a return spring.

A pole lathe can be made by any competent carpenter with some assistance from the blacksmith. Such low capital cost has enabled trained wood turners to set up in business for themselves with the least possible funding. In England, their hovels and small work huts have echoed to the rattle and whirr of their lathes for more than a thousand years. Nonetheless, there are some further points which ought to be made here. Compared with a continuously rotating treadle lathe, pole lathes are wasteful in terms both of energy and of time. Contrary to what GW Lailey himself said, and which has been repeated even by pole lathe practitioners in recent times, there is no function or process which can be better done on a pole lathe than on a continuously rotating lathe, whether man-driven by treadle and flywheel or, of course, by power. In short, negligible capital cost and (with some types) easy portability are a pole lathe's most valuable properties, not its capabilities as a machine.

Before making a brief survey of early pole lathes, one of which is undoubtedly ancestral to Lailey's lathe, we will look first at another which is both contemporary with the last Lailey and was in use up to the last war.

17A. Albert Carter at his chair bodger's lathe in 1937. *Reading 35/5895*.

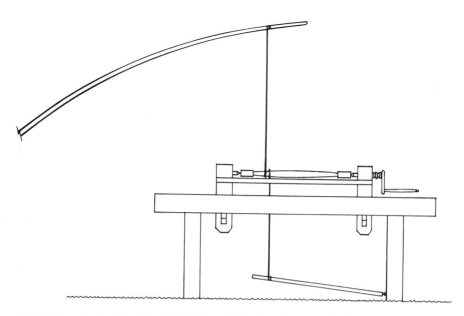

17B. Schematic drawing of a chair bodger's lathe from the turner's side.

Figure 17 has Albert Carter at work on a lathe very similar to the portable ones used around High Wickham by the chair bodgers. Indeed, the work done on it was of the same nature.

The turnpiece is driven by a sash cord which leads from the tip of a springy pole or sapling, passes once round it, and goes thence to a treadle. As with all bodger's lathes (though not with bowl turner's lathes) the turner sits at his work. Pressing down with his left foot, the workpiece is rotated downwards towards him. As it does so, the chisel or turning tool is advanced slightly across the toolrest and the material is cut. The tool is withdrawn at the end of the down stroke by a small amount to avoid a braking action on the contra rotating workpiece and abrasion on the cutting edge of the chisel. The whole operation takes place much faster than these words can be read: 100 to 120 such strokes a minute would be normal. Long practice has co-ordinated the turner's movements and the sound of the process is very like zz-zz-zz...as this is read. The floor-to-floor time for making a chair leg is about 4 minutes. They were always turned from prepared material, that is from staves of cleft wood made as nearly as possible round in section with a draw knife. Heart wood was never used.

In the thirties, most of Albert Carter's work was for repairs and replacements. The lathe he is using is somewhat heavier than the original

41

bodger's lathes. These were of similar form but lighter, as the generality of chair bodgers worked in hovels in the woodland, moving from coppice to coppice in the beech woods each season and their machines had to be truly portable. The legs and rails which they made were for the manufacture of Windsor chairs; the rest of the work, seats, arms and the assembly, being done in permanent buildings, especially in High Wickham, Buckinghamshire. By the inter-war period, most, if not all, bodgers had built corrugated iron huts for themselves in that neighbourhood and the cleft timber was brought from the woods to these workshops (5). A certain number of legs and rails were for stools and the like.

The Windsor chair itself, which dates from *c* 1700, was designed for turned parts. The wood used was normally beech. This has the ability when machined green to dry out in its turned form without undue distortion. In this small diameter work, the extra weight of the green wood was of no consequence. The lathes themselves were akin to those much more massive types used in earlier times for Jacobean and similar heavy table legs and bed posts, one of which is noticed below.

Reverting to Roman times and the historic sequence of lathe turning thereafter, whilst few turned artefacts have survived (though Dr Morris has identified some in such woods as apple), we have nonetheless certain evidence of heavy work in the unlikely form of a number of cast bronze tables and in depictions of stools with turned legs. The bronze legs are clearly copies of turned wooden ones. Whether these were themselves finished on some form of lathe, we do not know: but the wooden patterns used for the moulds must have been turned (6). Moreover, their weight and intricacy would have involved machines a great deal heavier than the Ptolemaic lathe. Cranks and driving mechanisms not yet having been invented, pole-lathes are a possible answer, but there is no evidence to support it. With slave labour available, a turnpiece, held between centres, and strap-rotated by two men seems more likely. Such patterns are one-off jobs for making an indefinite number of castings.

It is in the Late Iron Age period that the so-called 'Dorset coal money' appears. The material used was Kimmeridge shale, a soft and machineable stone. The British Museum has not only the rings and discs (probably made for magical as well as ornamental purposes) but also the parted-off waste. It is the latter which originated the 'coal money' notion. The turning tools would have been flint-tipped. This is the first true turning known in Britain (7). Doubtless wood was also turned, but nothing has survived save for some Iron Age artefacts from Glastonbury. These last were most likely to have been made on a proto-lathe, or as in Egypt in pre-Ptolemaic times (above), as may also the Dorset 'coal money' have been.

The arrival of the Anglo-Saxon migrants brought wooden bowl turning for general domestic use to Britain and the commencement of the bowl-turning trade which was to end with the last Lailey at Bucklebury. (The words 'general domestic use' must be emphasized as Dr Morris has pointed out that bowl fragments have been found from earlier times, but these were either highly ornamental (Glastonbury) or toiletry articles in woods such as apple (Roman times). It is more than likely that these objects were turned on proto-lathes or on strap-driven lathes). The next chapter deals with wooden bowl turning and its history. No certain remains or drawings of any bowl turning lathe have been identified before the 13th century but the fragments of turned wooden bowls occur at many sites.

Apart from the paternosterer's rosary bead proto-lathe (Figure 15) we have two further representations of lathes from the Middle Ages: one is in a stained glass window in Chartres cathedral; the other, which is of the greatest importance to the theme of this study, comes from *La Bible Moralisée*, generally considered to be Anglo-Norman. (One half of this work is in the Bodleian Library at Oxford; the other is in the Bibliothèque Nationale at Paris).

18. The Chartres lathe, *c* 1250.
This is probably a similar lathe to Albert Carter's but the artist has not understood, nor has he succeeded in depicting, what he saw. *After Singer.*

The Chartres example *c* 1250 (Figure 18) is undoubtedly a pole lathe but lacks essential details such as a tool to do the turning. The turner, who is seated, has both hands on a large roller. His feet rest on what appears to be a treadle. Dr Morris, in her 1984 Cambridge dissertation, suggested that this indicates a crank drive (despite the obvious driving strap of a pole lathe). Unfortunately, crank drives with connecting rods were unknown in western Europe until another century had passed. The probable explanation is that this is an early version of a bodger's lathe (like Albert Carter's, Figure 17), with an exagerated turnpiece, and that its methodology was beyond the artist's understanding or his ability to depict.

The representation in *La Bible Moralisée c* 1250 (Figure 19) is the very first to depict a bowl turner. Schematically, his lathe is identical with Lailey's and Jordan's machines (described below). The tailstock (which carries the lefthand centre as viewed) should have been moveable. The outboard leg is off-picture, to the left as viewed. The tool rest would have been out of sight behind the part-turned bowl, as also the turner's hands and turning tool. To show the tool, the artist has caused his model to hold it higher up in an impossible position. Amazingly, exactly the same thing happened in certain photographs of both Lailey and Jordan (the Salopian turner, noted later). One can almost hear the 20th century photographer saying 'Hold your hands higher, Mr Lailey/Jordan, I can't get the tool into the frame'. The monkish illustrator who drew this picture for his Bible doubtless made a similar request to his bowl turner subject. (Figures 28 and 29 have Lailey and Jordan as described. Note also Figure 20 where a Dutch turner's hands, tool and tool rest are all hidden by the turnpiece). This important Anglo-Norman lathe will be noticed again in the next chapter. If it is reasonable to suggest that such lathes as this one would not have altered very much since the Migration Period, we can clearly claim continuity between the trade of bowl turning in Anglo-Saxon times and that of the Laileys of Bucklebury - a trade finally extinguished within living memory.

No doubt there were wide variations in the types of pole or reciprocating lathes used in different areas and at different times, but there were only two basically disparate forms. These were the Reading type, with a massive headstock, non-portable and capable of turning the largest diameters of bowl, as will be described in actuality below: and a lighter sort with both headstock and tailstock moveable. Those of this second kind were themselves of two designs, one having a bed consisting of two rails as with a bodger's lathe (Figure 17) and the other with a heavy slab

19. A mediaeval bowl turner, *c* 1250.

As drawn by the artist, the machine is far too light for the size of bowl depicted. Just as in Jordan's photograph (Figure 29) the tool is being held so as to suit the artist. The outboard leg supporting the lathe bed is out- of-picture to the left. The turner is correctly shown with his left foot on the treadle. Schematically, this is the Reading Lathe and it antedates all other representations of a pole lathe by 400 years or so, save only the Chartres lathe (Figure 18). Note the sapling acting as a return spring and the drive belt (probably leather) correctly shown so that the turnpiece rotates *towards* the turner when the treadle is depressed. The original comes from a work entitled '*La Bible Moralisée*', Vol.II, which is in the Bibliothèque Nationale, Paris, (Vol.I being in the Bodleian Library, Oxford). *Reproduced by the permission of the Bibliothèque Nationale, Paris.*

bed as in Figure 20, used by a turner of table legs, working in the Netherlands, *c* 1600. This lathe has a very solid base of timber with a slot running longitudinally along the centre line. The whole is supported on splay legs, an unexpected feature for a machine in a well-built workshop. The prototype was likely to have been a portable woodland, or bodger's lathe, now massively built to handle the heavy workpiece, a Jacobean table leg.

20. A Dutch turner of heavy table legs, *c* 1600.
This carved panel shows a heavy pole lathe. There is a strong resemblance to James Davies' lathe in Figure 21. This pole lathe is of the type with two moveable stocks and has a slab bed in place of the more usual pair of horizontal rails. The two stocks appear to be rather light for so massive a bed. *After Singer.*

A similar lathe, but very much lighter (Figure 21) is to be seen in Pinto (1949) where a Welsh turner is working on a platter. This form was used by Dr Carole Morris for her experimental bowl turning on a pole lathe. Such lathes are much too light for the large diameters of work commonly done by Lailey and Jordan, or for the sizes of bowl known from Anglo-Saxon times (briefly referred to later), or indeed for Jacobean table legs.

Figure 22 has another Dutch turner at work *c* 1650 on an ordinary chair leg. Except that the tool rest is arranged for cylindrical turning, this machine is very close to Lailey's and Jordan's lathes. There is even a bowl fixed to the top of the headstock exactly as at Bucklebury and as now in the Reading University Museum. The bed is formed from two members and, as always with this type, is capable of turning much longer objects. By using an alternative toolrest, this machine is an adequate one for bowl turning and was evidently so used.

21. A Welsh turner, *c* 1905.
James Davies of Abercuch, a Welsh turner, working on a (probably sycamore, judging by the long shavings) platter. To the right, is a larger diameter bowl. This has an angle between the sides and bottom, which means that the whole interior has been turned away. Some of his general production, Welsh type ladles with hook handles, is in the background. Note the lightness of the two stocks (the lathe not being of the Reading type). This means that heavy removal of wood took a long time as each cut must have been correspondingly light. It would also indicate that bowls and platters were only occasional products, or he would have mounted stronger stocks. This lathe closely resembles the Dutch one in Figure 20. Notice that the turner is holding the tool in an impossible position (a good foot away from his turnpiece), doubtless to oblige the photographer. *Photograph from the National Museum of Wales.*

This concludes the historical review of reciprocating lathes. From *c* 1500 the treadle-and-crank and the great-wheel drives came into use. Leonardo da Vinci (1452-1519) designed a treadle-and-crank lathe. Both types provided the turner with a continuously rotating workpiece which thus more than halved the total turning time. Figures 23 and 24 have such lathes. They were ideal for fine work, though the great-wheel type doubled the man-hours as an assistant was required to provide the drive as in Egypt twelve centuries before, though rather more efficiently.

Da Vinci's treadle design is exemplified by the 18th century lathe in Figure 24. This form was much used for fine work such as clockmaking

22. Another Dutch turner, *c* 1650.

The artist has shown him with the wrong foot on the treadle. He is turning a light chair leg and thus has a toolrest appropriate for the purpose, similar to Albert Carter's (Figure 17). The lathe is of the Reading type, with a strong fixed headstock. The bowl fixed to this (as at Reading, Figure 25) indicates that he does such turning and the general construction of his machine is adequate for this purpose. As well as a different toolrest, mandrels would have been required to make bowls. *After Singer.*

and ivory turning. These machines were most elegantly built in mahogany and brass. The treadle rotates a large wheel, its weight acting as a flywheel to carry the reciprocating stroke of the connecting rod through the top and bottom dead centre points. What such a lathe lacked was the cast iron technology of the 19th century. Once cast iron engineer's lathes were available, accurately machined flywheels running on smooth bearings allowed continuously rotating treadle lathes to be built which halved the time and effort of the wooden bowl turner. Many of the Welsh turners used them (8); the same men whose descendants converted to power driven lathes in later times.

We must briefly refer to the application of power to turning. The first known use of water power, other than for flour milling or fulling cloth, was a sawmill at Augsburg in south Germany, recorded in 1337. It is thought that the first water-driven turneries were established some time in the 17th century. The numbers were never very great as turning was largely a matter of an invididual craftsman setting up within easy reach of his raw material supplies, but such enterprises were still in operation in the 19th century in the Wye Valley, in Cumberland and in Yorkshire. These workshops depended upon three factors: a source of water power; material close at hand; a not too distant market for the turner's products. The coming of steam and, later, gas engines seems to have passed the rural craft turners by, but the electrical distribution network, post 1918, was welcomed by the Welsh turners.

Few, if any of the Welshmen were primarily bowl makers as was Lailey, and their trade in other turnery such as spoons, small ladles, platters and the like, formed the larger part of their output. Their workshops tended to be located in villages and not in the woodlands. Their largest turned objects were within the swing afforded by the cheaper forms of cast iron treadle lathes (8) and when electricity arrived in their area, power was readily applied. Meanwhile, their continuing trade seems to have remained based on the utility value of their products rather than any notion of craftsmanship and this was what sold them. Thus, departing from pole-lathes meant great savings of time and energy to the turners and was of little or no significance to their customers.

The question presents itself, why did the seemingly more conservative English bowl turners and chair bodgers not follow the example of the Welshmen? In the case of the bodgers (who represent the largest body of woodland turners in England between the wars), their work was all small diameter stuff, sitting-down work. A cast iron treadle lathe would

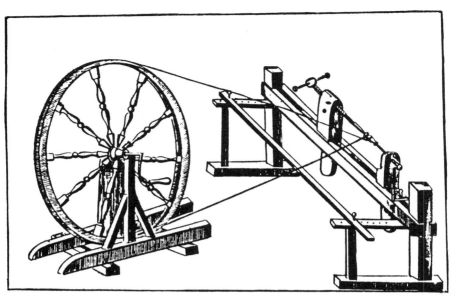

23. A great-wheel lathe, *c* 1700.
Pinto considered that the later ornamental mazers and loving-cups were turned on this type of lathe. The woods used became harder and ultimately included Lignum Vitae from the West Indies. The view is taken here that such lathes were essential for the fine finishing of the harder woods but that the main weight of material removal was still done on pole lathes. After Moxon's *Mechanik Exercises*, published in 1703.

certainly have increased their throughput. But the cost of such a machine would have been about fifty times that of a pole lathe. It would also have been a heavy and awkward load to transport from place to place in the soggy woodland where they worked. In earlier days, therefore, the capital cost and the lack of portability would have been decisive as the bodgers moved annually from coppice to coppice. In later times when they operated in corrugated iron huts (rather than in wood and turf structures of the bivouac type), the lack of capital in a dying trade would have had the same effect. The huts were always well out of reach of electric power.

Before 1914, a great part of the Lailey's trade had depended on the mystique of 'Hand made'. After the temporary reversion during the war to a practical basis alone, GW Lailey's customers were again those who revered craftsmanship, and he knew this very well. HV Morton, writing in 1927, said that to enter Lailey's workshop was to be transported back to Anglo-Saxon times.

A great admirer of the Bucklebury bowl turner, Col WJ Julyan,

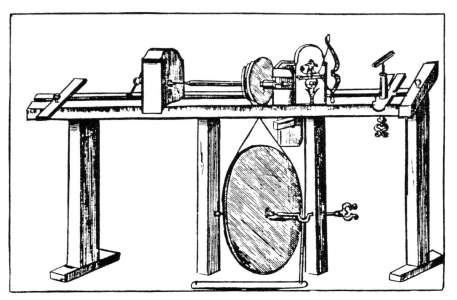

24. A treadle lathe, *c* 1700.
These lathes were used only for small, accurate work. Later models, built in mahogany and brass, achieved quite high precision. It is unlikely that such lathes were ever used for bowl turning. But they may have been employed for small trinket bowls or similar, hollow objects. Cast iron technology was needed to make such lathes truly versatile. After Moxon's *Mechanik Exercises*, published in 1703.

presented him in the late thirties with a steel stamp with the words 'Hand made' which he could apply to the bases of his bowls. He soon threw it away, saying that his customers preferred to have his signature and the date instead (9). (See Frontispiece).

Figure 25 shows the Reading Lathe as it stands today and Figure 26 indicates its mechanical features. The hemispherical blank is mounted between the centres with the addition of a mandrel. This enables rotation to be applied to the workpiece from the leather driving strap or belt. The blank is arranged for the first turning operation, the outside of the bowl. The second view has the blank/mandrel assembly reversed for the second such operation, the trepanning of the interior. Figure 27 illustrates the entire sequence of manufacture, excluding the breaking out of the core and finishing. This drawing also shows all Lailey's extant mandrels together with his largest one (conjectured from photographs). All but this one may be seen at Reading today.

A series of bowls, usually four, was turned from the same hemispherical

25. The Reading Lathe today.

This is the centrepiece of the Museum attached to the Rural History Centre at the University of Reading. (For labelled details, see Figure 26).

The original headstock ends at the joint which is visible about a foot above the boards of the present plinth. This, and the buttress pieces were added when the machine was moved from position B1 to B2 as indicated approximately in Figure 7. This was done $c$ 1930, the lower part of the then earthfast baulk having rotted away during the century or so that it had stood in the hotbed of shavings on the floor of the pit. To secure the lathe, struts at each end were fixed to the W wall behind the turner. The lower part of this wall was eventually destroyed by the continual vibrations transmitted to it and was covered by corrugated iron sheeting as may be seen in Figure 10. The outboard supporting leg is modern.

The hollow in the bed seen in the RH picture has been caused by the turner in his later years (probably from $c$ 1945) using it to finish chipping his hemispherical blanks, instead of doing all this either in the open or in the upper part of the hut (where the light was now very poor due to the closing of the N window when the hut was re-clad, $c$ 1937). But the outside chipping block remained and was probably used for the first rough chipping. This block (a substantial tree stump) may be seen in Figure 1, and in Figure 5 Lailey has a bowl resting on it.

The saplings used for poles lasted for up to 10 years. The peripatetic chair bodgers cut a new one each year and seasoned it for 6 months before use. The present pole is that removed from the hut in 1959. After 30 years in dry and heated atmospheres it must be somewhat fragile. With a new pole, the lathe would be perfectly usable today. The treadle would then be in its 'ready-use' position, about 15in from the floor.

In the lefthand picture, the tray on the lathe bed carries the extant mandrels, together with a group of hook tools. Note the small bowl fixed on the top of the headstock (exactly as with the Dutch turner $c$ 1650 in Figure 22). This held an oil bottle (for lubricating the fixed centres), sandpaper, a lump of carnauba wax (for polishing the bowl rims) and a carpenter's pencil.

*Photographs by the University of Reading Photographic Unit, 1994.*

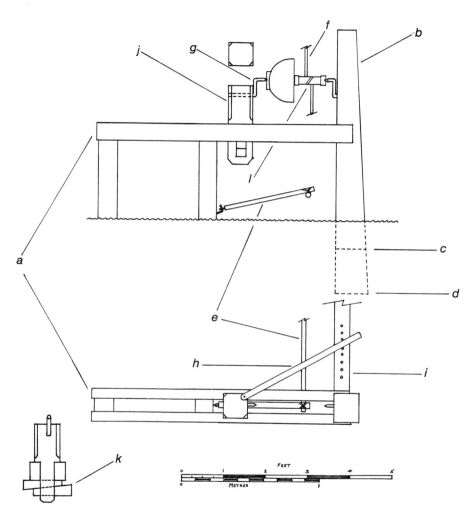

26. Elevation and plan of the Reading Lathe showing mechanical features.
a. lathe bed of two beams (original). b. headstock (original). c. present height of headstock.
d. estimated height of headstock in position B1 in Figure 7 (then earthfast). e. two-member
treadle. f. drive belt. g. centres raised from pre-$c$ 1904 position using cranks. h. toolrest.
i. support for toolrest. j. tailstock (replaced $c$ 1930). k. double wedges for anchoring tailstock.
l. mandrel (original).

blank. Lailey always claimed that this was his method and he is so recorded by Woods. However, while Figure 28 has him with an exhibition workpiece of four such bowls, turned but not yet broken out at their cores, Figure 29 has Robert ("Jack") Jordan, the Wellington, Salop, turner with an identical set-up on an identical lathe. The fact is that neither seems to have been aware of the other's existence.

Robert ("Jack") Jordan at Wellington, Salop, was contemporary with Lailey. Two years older (b. 1867), he worked at bowl turning on an identical lathe. This was in the timber yard of R. Groom, Sons & Co. Ltd., where he had been an employee for some 54 years when the photograph reproduced in Figure 29 was taken. Whereas Lailey turned bowls only in elm wood, most of Jordan's were from sycamore (which is a little easier to turn). Here we have a bowl turner using a pole lathe situated where there had been power supplies for many years and where the owners would hardly have noticed the expense of providing him with a modern cast iron turning lathe. It is clear that the sale of his output was dependent upon its origin, an ancient craftsman operating a lathe of a design directly descended from those of his Anglo-Saxon forebears. At the time when this picture was published in conjunction with a short article, the lathe and the turner were booked to be part of an exhibit at the Royal Agricultural Society's forthcoming Show at Wolverhampton in 1937 (10).

Both the Reading Lathe and that at Wellington are the direct descendants of the industry of bowl turning which started in England with the Anglo-Saxon Migration, and the machine shown at Reading is the only survivor.

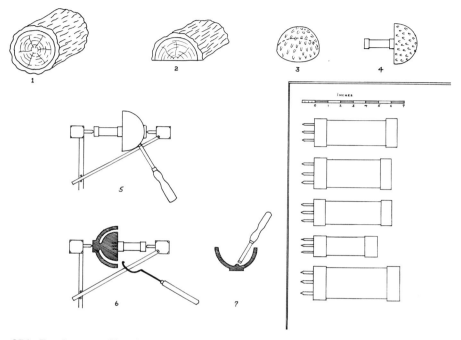

27A. *Turning nested bowls.*
1. The billet from the tree. 2. The billet is split down its axis. 3. The half-round is made into a hemisphere by axe. 4. A mandrell is driven into the prepared piece. 5. The outside of the bowl is turned. 6. The workpiece assembly is reversed and the bowl is trepanned. 7 .The parting pip is removed.
NOTE: not shown are sanding, edge cleaning and carnauba waxing of the rim.
Inset
*Lailey's mandrels*
The first four mandrels are those extant. The fifth (lowest) one is conjectural from photographs of Lailey turning exhibition bowl sets. Godfrey Eke carried out trials on the actual lathe and found that the absolute maximum diameter, beyond which the belt would overrun itself, was about $2^3/_4$in. So this has been drawn at $2^1/_2$in diameter as the likely size that was used. These mandrels are of sycamore and have iron rings shrunk on the ends by the blacksmith to avoid splitting. The small ones are hollowed by use.

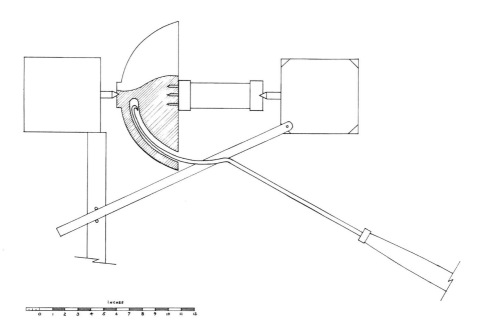

27B. A larger view of the inside turning showing the action of a hook tool. Lailey made the curve in the tool himself, using trial and error methods until it generated the correct shape.

28. (On facing page) GW Lailey with an exhibition workpiece, *c* 1929.
Lailey with a nest of bowls. This has been specially turned in one piece for exhibition purposes. This sort of thing is pure bravura and entails tremendous labour. In practice, the entire core of the largest bowl would have been removed as soon as possible to reduce the weight of the following turnpiece. The lathe is in its original east to west position and the corrugated iron wall of the north side of the hut may be seen through the chink in the partition behind the turner. The original negative of this photograph has been lost *Reading 35/26371*.

29. Robert ('Jack') Jordan, the Wellington, Salop, turner exhibiting a nest of bowls on a lathe identical to Lailey's. Note that, for photographic purposes, he is holding his turning tool well above its correct place on the toolrest (the end of which may be seen on top of the tailstock), when the tool would not have been visible. Something similar has happened in Figure 19 where the Anglo-French illuminator has posed his model in the same way. Original from the Wellington Journal & Shrewsbury News, published 8.5.37. *Reading 35/5380*.

# NOTES on Chapter Two

1. It would seem natural to call this man a slave, but Dr Helen Whitehouse has pointed out that what we know of the social conditions of the time indicates that he would have been a free man. Underprivileged, he may have been, but not servile: perhaps a kind of apprentice.

2. Lucas, 1962.

3. Singer, Vol. I, p.193.

4. Gordon V Childe, J Geraint Jenkins, are examples.

   Childe in Singer, imagined the lathe drive delivered from a weighted descending bucket. He was undoubtedly right about the bucket as suitable saplings would have been rare in Egypt but did not realize that the pole it replaced was not the driving force. However, there is no evidence for any lathe with a spring return system of any kind in classical Egypt. Jenkins prints a photograph captioned, 'The pole, the driving power of the lathe'. (1965) Figure 10.

5. Edlin, Jenkins, Arnold and author's recollections.

6. Singer, Vol II, p.223.

7. Oakley, 1949 p.87.

8. Jenkins, 1965 p.62.

9. Private correspondence with Mrs Meg Cooper, a distant relative of Lailey.

10. Wellington Journal and Shrewsbury News, 1937.

## Chapter Three

# Bowl turning from Anglo-Saxon times

The various continental peoples who (in small numbers) came to Britain in the 4th century did so in the main as officials and soldiers. These were absorbed by the Romano-British civilization which still flourished. By about 410, this had collapsed and with it went the well-established industrial potteries, such as that in the Nene Valley. The products were wheel-thrown on a fast wheel and fired in quite sophisticated kilns. These techniques were beyond the competance of the wave of immigrants which started c 420: wheel-thrown pottery was not to reappear for another two hundred years (1). The incomers needed pots for two main purposes: for cooking and some culinary purposes, and for interring the ashes of their dead. For the first, they employed a hand modelling process and used the most primitive method of all, coiling the clay. These pots were fired in clamps. They were stacked, and brushwood piled over them was ignited. The generally used term for this is 'bonfire pottery'. For long after comparatively good wares were being made on the slow wheel (Ipswich ware, c 650), and even after much superior pots had achieved wide distribution (fast wheel-thrown vessels such as Thetford ware, c 850), this handmade stuff continued well into the Anglo-Saxon period.

The need for urns was filled in three ways: continental imports; very carefully hand-modelled urns, taking a lot of time and trouble; and, in the west country later on, burying the ashes in hollow wooden vessels (2).

Common domestic Saxon ware, especially that of the Pagan Period, is so crudely made that excavators of ancient sites have remarked that it is well below the standard to be expected from a first year pottery class at any High School today, (Figure 30). But any settlement, however small, could either make its own utensils or use the services of an itinerant potter. The continental immigrants also brought with them their long-established skills in wooden bowl-turning for basic domestic purposes. The view is taken here that it was these abilities that had inhibited their forebears from taking much interest in pottery, and this approach continued for the first two centuries from the beginning of the Migration Period.

Pottery sherds are nearly indestructible. The natural end for the fragments of a broken wooden bowl or of the turner's waste was as kindling for the fire. Even when discarded with other rubbish, wood being an organic substance survives only when special conditions obtain, in a

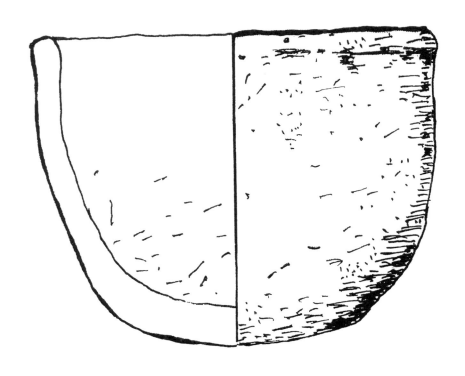

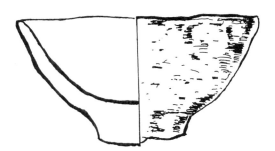

30. Anglo-Saxon handmade pottery.
The top drawing is of a typical cooking pot of globular form, marked externally by fire, and comes from Hut 85 at Mucking. It measures about 8 $\frac{1}{2}$" (22cm) dia.
The lower, a small dish, is from Hut 42 at the same site. It measures about 5in (13cm) dia.
*After JG Hirst.*

bog or in sterile soil. In England, such conditions are rare and mostly to be found for example in the detritus at the bottom of a well. Archaeological research recovers immense quantities of sherds: over 12,000 came from West Stow, Suffolk and over 30,000 from the Mucking, Essex, sites. Only a few hundred parts of wooden bowls belonging to the entire pre-Conquest period have come to light. Inevitably, this leads to a very lopsided picture of artefacts in use within a household. The reality is that all were well supplied with wooden bowls both for wet and for dry purposes. For carrying and holding water, extensive use was made of coopered wooden buckets (Jean Cook, forthcoming). At the end of the Anglo-Saxon period, in that part of the Bayeux Tapestry which shows Bishop Odo blessing the food for the Duke's guests, a number of bowls are in use and these are clearly turned wooden bowls for the most part.

The minuscule number of wooden bowl fragments from the early first millennium AD grows from time to time. Because the numbers are small, analysed percentages are liable to change from their apparent precision with the identification of only a small number of new fragments. But in Dr Morris's view (personal communication) the general picture has not altered for nearly ten years and this is shown in Table I.

*Table I (3)*

## Bowl fragments identified by wood used:

|  | 10th century and before | 11th to 15th century |
|---|---|---|
| Alder | 30% | 12% |
| Ash | 14 | 66 |
| Beech | 3.5 | 7 |
| Birch | 3.5 | 10 |
| Hazel | 27 | 2.5 |
| Maple (field) | 22 | 2.5 |
|  | 100% | 100% |

## Grouping the softer and harder woods:

| Alder, Birch, Hazel | 60.5% | SOFT | 24.5% |
|---|---|---|---|
| Ash, Beech, Maple | 39.5% | HARD | 75.5% |

The field Maple (*Acer campestris*) is a borderline case between hard and soft and perhaps ought to be counted as soft.

* In that case we have:

| | | | |
|---|---|---|---|
| Alder, Birch, Hazel and Maple | 82.5% | SOFT | 27% |
| Ash and Beech | 17.5% | HARD | 73% |
| | 100% | | 100% |

* In her experimental bowl turning on her own pole lathe, Dr Morris claims that Maple was no harder to turn than Alder. This is a useful trial result, although it applies to greenwood turning. Furthermore, she used modern tools of alloy steel, not Anglo-Saxon ones. See also Alder/Elm weights in Table III.

These figures come from finds on many sites. Unless new finds result in an enormous alteration in these proportions, one thing stands out very clearly, viz: between the first part of our period and the second, there was a very large change in usage from softer woods to harder woods for making bowls.

To provide a vignette of things during a later time, Table II lists the identities of the finds from Exeter. The total number is far too small for any general conclusions, but it does yield one new piece of information.

*Table II (4)*

Complete and incomplete bowls and platters from Goldsmith and Trinchay Streets, Exeter, (up to 1984) dated *c* 1300 onwards.

| | |
|---|---|
| Ash | 1 |
| Elm | 5 |
| Lime | 1 |
| Maple | 9 |
| | 16 |

These numbers contain a fact of some importance: elm at last appears. Thereafter, there is a gap of perhaps one hundred years unfilled by any surviving relic of elm turnery. Nonetheless, this is the forerunner of its large scale use during the post-Tudor time when the platter and bowl turning industry became an essentially country thing after pewter came into general use. The other wood most used was now the ornamental sycamore (*Acer pseudoplatanus*) which first appears in England near the end of the 16th century. Both these woods are harder and more durable than the soft woods extensively employed for bowls in earlier times. Here is a brief review of the properties of the various woods mentioned from the viewpoint of the turning of domestic articles and of some other uses:

*Alder*　　　This is a very soft wood, easy to turn, capable of making very thin walled hollow vessels. It is liable to split during the turning process and afterwards. It does not make a durable article. In modern times, virtually its only uses were for river bank revetting and for making the soles of clogs. These indicate its one advantage, its ability to withstand wet conditions. This is perhaps why it also suited Anglo-Saxon culinary usage. It is also a very light wood for turning, (see Table III).

*Birch*　　　These have similar properties to alder, with hazel being an
*Hazel*　　　even poorer wood than alder. None has the ability of alder
*& Lime*　　　to cope with wet. Since the 18th century, hazel has been considered useless for any manufacturing purpose.

*Maple*　　　The field maple is somewhat harder than the above woods and turns well. It was so extensively used in many ways that the tree population declined. Its place was taken by sycamore (*c* 1600), a far superior wood for turnery.

*Sycamore*　The ornamental sycamore (Acer pseudoplatanus) appeared in England at the end of the 16th century and has been used for bowl turning down to modern times. Whilst it has adequate resistance to wet conditions, it does not stand up very well to really rough usage. It is a harder wood than the field maple. It was Jordan's main raw material.

*Ash*　　　　This is a harder wood than any of those previously mentioned. Its normal use for many hundreds of years down to modern times is for tool handles and axe helves. It is extensively used for ornamental bowl turning today as it shows very fine grain patterning when polished. It is the hardest of the woods listed in Table I. When turned as a bowl across the grain (as are all bowls, but not all platters), it has a tendency to split, but the chance of its doing so is small and not to be compared with that of the softer woods, particularly alder, however carefully these are inspected for flaws and shakes beforehand.

*Elm*

As noted, the first elm bowls were being turned before the 14th century. It is much harder than any of the previous woods. It can accept quite closely spaced holes without the least danger of its splitting. Hence its use for wheel hubs from the times of the Pharaohs of Egypt for chariot wheels until this century for horse-drawn carts. It has excellent wet-and-dry capabilities and was thus used for the keels and garboard strakes of wooden ships. For nearly a century and a half, the Lailey family used it exclusively for bowls to stand the roughest treatment and to hold liquids. It takes a lot more hard effort to produce a fine finish and a thin section. This, the Laileys never attempted as their work was entirely geared to domestic products for practical use, though many a Lailey bowl was refinished and polished by his customers. Elm makes good wooden platters, able to take the roughest kitchen and scullery usage. Platters of this wood in the Pinto Collection at Birmingham go back to the 17th century. The earliest are part of a 200 piece set from Sussex. Many a Lailey bowl, regularly used for washing-up purposes in the butler's pantry and in the scullery, has been recorded as lasting for 30 years and more. Recently, it has been claimed that a Lailey bowl had been in regular use for washing fine china for about 60 years before its replacement by a plastic one. (Mrs Meg Cooper in correspondence).

*Beech*

The use of beech for chair components, together with its special property of being turnable when green without subsequent distortion has already been noted. From the days of automatic machinery, many millions of components have been annually turned in this wood - from shoe lasts and high heels for ladies shoes to furniture components to clothes pegs and many kitchen utensils which are nowadays made principally of plastic materials. (Though turnery from modern machinery demands kiln-dried timber to about 5 per cent MC as for most products subsequent shrinkage is unacceptable).

Although its general turning qualities are akin to those of elm, it does not possess the ability to withstand immersion in water. Its use for bowls is very rare as in this form it is liable to split. It is essentially a wood for solid objects rather than hollow vessels. The High Wickham furniture industry was dependent on beech for a very long time. The legs and rails were stacked in the open to air-dry after turning.

*Hornbeam*   This is far and away the hardest native English wood. It was rarely used for bowls until better (alloy) steel for tools and treadle or powered lathes became available, and then for ornamental, rather than domestic, artefacts; but its use for specially high quality shoe lasts between the wars may be noted, and these have been turned on exceedingly sophisticated machines for nearly a century, now.

It has been said that the species of the locally available timber is the sole determinant of what was used to make wooden bowls at any particular period. This must be right insofar as it is well known that before the 19th century timber was seldom transported further than twenty miles from its place of use. It cannot be an absolute criterion as otherwise we would find beech bowls being made in the Chilterns and the Cotswolds, and ash bowls in large areas of Northamptonshire and Rutland where the ash predominates. More than half of the identified bowl fragments from the 10th century and before which are listed in Table I are of soft woods, unsatisfactory in turning and lacking the ability to stand up to rough usage. More than three quarters of those listed from the 11th century are of harder woods having far greater durability. Elm, one of the two or three best woods for domestic bowls and platters is rarely found before modern times. This may be a mere matter of chance as recovered bowl fragments from Norman to Tudor times are very few. But in view of the Exeter finds, there is a strong suspicion that the large quantities of cups and platters documented from mediaeval times (Chapter Five) were largely of elm. But no proof of this can at the moment be offered. As already seen, Lailey's lathe, in use in this century, equates to one illustrated in the 13th century and it is a not unreasonable assumption that his was in no way superior to those used by Anglo-Saxon bowl-turners. Some other variable must be found and this can lie only in the tools used.

To examine this point it is simplest to work backwards in time. Most, if not all, of Lailey's tools, exhibited now at Reading, came from his grandfather. The cutting tips wore out from time to time and these were replaced by the local blacksmith. For this purpose, he used material from old files. These were cut up and welded to the shank of the tool by the cut-and-shut method, and then re-hardened. It may be noted that woodworking tools from any toolstore today are far superior in terms of wear resistance to anything Lailey used as they are universally of alloy steel.

It is recorded that Lailey once turned without charge a quantity of oak bowls to be sold for charity. The wood came from the beams taken from a Newbury church roof affected by the death watch beetle. Being several centuries old, this wood can scarcely have been harder to turn. He complained strongly, not of the extra labour involved in the turning, but of the frequency with which he lost the edge on his tools and was obliged to re-sharpen them. Never again, he is recorded as saying, would he do anything 'for charity'. (Julyan, in correspondence on file at Reading).

Improvements in steel making over the thirteen hundred years from Anglo-Saxon times until the 18th century were both irregular and slow. In Dr G Macdonnell's view, steel before $c$ 1000 was superior to what we know was used both in the preceding Romano-British era and in succeeding centuries right down to the 18th. This would seem to be contrary to the suggestion above that the very notable change from softer to harder woods centred upon the 10th/11th centuries was concerned with steel quality. Appendix B attempts to resolve this apparent contradiction.

There are two aspects of Anglo-Saxon bowl-turning which require further consideration. First, there are a number of bowls which have cracked and have been repaired, either by one or more staples, or by a rim clip of bronze. Such repairs as the last come from graves and are the only indication that a bowl or goblet had been buried, the actual wood having perished. In later graves, a complete rim mount or edging occurs. At one time, it was thought that these utensils (considered to be drinking vessels) were placed only in male graves, but Morris has pointed out that they have been found in at least two female graves. The placing of a repaired drinking cup in a grave would seem to indicate that it had been a personal (and perhaps, favourite) possession of the deceased.

One in nine of the bowl fragments of turner's waste from the Coppergate, York, excavation had a crack in it and Morris found that, out of a grand total of 323 bowl fragments from many sites, 18 of them had been repaired by stapling. She suggests that these defects were due to the bowls having been turned from green (that is, unseasoned) wood and that they are the proof of this. The point is discussed below, but the view taken here is that much cracking originated in the poor quality of the timber used, alder wood in particular, and that this was the consequence of the need for easy turning with inferior tools. The very use of alder betokens poor tools: there cannot have been a shortage of such better material as field maple which accounts for about one third of the finds. Rim mounts or edgings are usually found without any trace of the wood which formed the cup or bowl. At best, there is just an odd fibre of wood still adherent to the metal. The amount of work required to make and fit such a rim may mean that the vessel had been turned from one of the better woods in the first place. As the finds are all from graves and no particular wood can yet be identified, this again can lead to distortion of our picture of what materials the turners used and of their methods of manufacture. The use of staples to repair bowls is akin to the rivetting of china, an art still practised in this century.

Turning to the second aspect of Anglo-Saxon craftsmanship in bowl-turning (which is the question of green or airdried wood) involves a backward look from modern times. Lailey worked exclusively in elm which had been seasoned for several years. There is no record of any bowl of his ever having split. There were a few damaged bowls among those collected from Lailey's workshop by Reading in 1959, but these were due either to mechanical breakage or to a basic timber defect such as a knot: none had split. Since Jordan, who used an identical lathe to produce bowls of similar size in sycamore (the ornamental variety), was located in a timber yard there is no reason to suppose that he did otherwise (5). The only timber which can successfully be turned green and afterwards dried is beech, and then only as reduced to the dimensions of chair legs and stretchers.

It is unthinkable that either of these turners would have put the work into, say, a 12in (30cm) diameter bowl only to have it split afterwards. It may be noted here that Jordan in his late 50s required the extra help of a second man on a double treadle for the larger sizes by reason of the weight of the workpiece as will now be explained. There is no other evidence for such a practice either in modern times or in earlier centuries.

The reciprocating action of a pole lathe involves accelerating the workpiece from zero to cutting speed at each stroke. The angular momentum which has to be imparted to a blank for a chair leg in green beech is very low. The piece of wood weighs about $1\frac{1}{2}$ lb (0.7kg) and would be around $1\frac{1}{2}$ in (4cm) in diameter. This enables a bodger to work at a very high speed (as noted of Albert Carter in Chapter Two).

# TABLE III
## TABLE of MOISTURE CONTENT of VARIOUS WOODS
### used for turning bowls

| WOOD (1) | GREEN LBS/FT³ | % | AIRDRY LBS/FT³ | % | BAKED DRY LBS/FT³ (3) | |
|---|---|---|---|---|---|---|
| ALDER | 46 | 46 | 28 | 10 | 25 | (4) |
| ASH | 48 | 30 | 41 | 10 | 37 | |
| BEECH (2) | 54 | 32 | 45 | 10 | 41 | |
| BIRCH | 57 | 43 | 44 | 10 | 40 | |
| CEDAR | 37 | 23 | 33 | 10 | 30 | |
| CHESTNUT | 55 | 53 | 40 | 10 | 36 | |
| ELM | 53 | 33 | 44 | 10 | 40 | (4) |
| LARCH | 48 | 50 | 36 | 10 | 32 | |
| MAPLE (2) | 47 | 52 | 34 | 10 | 31 | |
| OAK | 63 | 50 | 47 | 10 | 42 | |
| PINE | 42 | 35 | 34 | 10 | 31 | |
| POPLAR | 38 | 52 | 28 | 10 | 25 | |
| SPRUCE | 34 | 36 | 28 | 10 | 25 | |
| SYCAMORE (2) | 52 | 67 | 34 | 10 | 31 | |
| WALNUT | 58 | 71 | 38 | 10 | 34 | |
| AVERAGES: | 49 | 44 | 38 | 10 | 34 | |
| NOTES: | | | | | | |

1.  All woods vary in weight according to country of origin, and where grown within it.
2.  Author's figures from 1930s:   Beech,        Central Europe
                                     Maple,        US and Canada
                                     Sycamore,     English
3.  As is done with all wood samples to obtain moisture content. This is much more accurate than the electronic method.
4.  Note especially that airdried elm has about the same weight per unit volume as wet (green) alder.

## TABLE IV
## WEIGHTS of BLANKS FOR BOWLS of VARIOUS DIAMETERS IN
### different woods

| Nom. dia. of bowl | | O/D of hemisphere | | Volume of hemisphere | | Sycamore Wt green | | 10% MC | | Elm Wt green | | 10% MC | |
|---|---|---|---|---|---|---|---|---|---|---|---|---|---|
| in | cm | in | cm | ft³ | m³ | lb | kg | lb | kg | lb | kg | lb | kg |
| 9 | | 10 | | 0.15 | | 8 | | 5 | | 8 | | 7 | |
| | 23 | | 25 | | 0.004 | | 3.5 | | 2.3 | | 3.6 | | 3.0 |
| 12 | | 13 | | 0.33 | | 17 | | 11 | | 17 | | 15 | |
| | 30 | | 33 | | 0.009 | | 7.8 | | 5.0 | | 7.9 | | 6.6 |
| 15 | | 17 | | 0.74 | | 38 | | 25 | | 39 | | 33 | |
| | 38 | | 43 | | 0.021 | | 17.5 | | 11.4 | | 17.8 | | 14.8 |
| 18 | | 20 | | 1.21 | | 63 | | 41 | | 64 | | 53 | |
| | 45 | | 50 | | 0.034 | | 28.6 | | 18.6 | | 29.1 | | 24.2 |

See also Table III.

*MC = moisture content*

From Table IV, it will be seen that an elm blank for a bowl having a nominal diameter of 18in (45cm) weighs 53 lbs (over 24kg) in airdried wood (10 per cent MC). It has an effective radius of rotation of about 4in (10cm), the point through which the weight of the block acts. The power input required varies as the cube, so that such a bowl needs eight times that of a 9in (23cm) one. Assuming that Lailey was using his treadle with its normal maximum stroke of about 15in (38cm) and his largest extant mandrel of $2^{1}/_{2}$in (6.5cm) diameter, and was working at a rate of 15 strokes a minute, the result is an energy output of around 1/15th HP ( 5.0 kg/m/sec) for an 18in (45cm) diameter bowl, which is about the greatest that a fit man can deliver continuously. If the blank is imagined as a green one, its weight rises to 64lb (29kg) and the required power input to nearly 1/12th HP (6.25kg/m/sec) which is greater than any ordinary man can sustain.

Various figures have been offered for the rate of splitting of alder or other softwood bowls when turned from green timber. These start at over 30% and come down to a claimed low point of 7%, depending on the skill of the operator and the careful selection of timber. It is even more difficult to conceive that during the whole six centuries of the Anglo-Saxon period, bowl-turners would not have discovered that seasoned wood of the harder sort can be turned without any loss at all, provided only that it is inspected first for cracks, flaws and shakes.

Bearing in mind that recovered bowl fragments tend to be those from smaller bowls rather than from the larger diameters, it is instructive to consider the size of a few of those which have been found: from Feddersen Wierde, Holland, before 450, two of nearly 14in (34cm) diameter; from London, c 900, 22in (55cm) diameter; from York, c 900, several over 12in (30cm) diameter.

Considering the London example of 22in (55cm) diameter (which came from the Bank of England site), the blank would have weighed around 110lb (50kg) in green maple. To turn it on a pole lathe would have required an energy input of about 1/5th HP (15.9kg/m /sec) which even two men on the treadle could hardly deliver. Turned from airdried wood, this drops to a more reasonable 1/13th HP (6.8kg/m/sec) provided the turning rate is no more than 10 strokes a minute. Lailey in his younger days is stated to have turned a number of 24in (60cm) diameter bowls, though this is unconfirmed by photographic or other evidence, except possibly for the Figure 3 photograph, but it is difficult to be sure. 20in (50cm) is more likely.

Hand turners today work in green wood on power lathes (where the weight of the turnpiece is of no consequence) and use the PEG method to dry them out. This is a post-war development and involves polyethelene glycol, a product of the chemical industry unavailable to turners of former times.

In short, Anglo-Saxon bowl-turners, would have used airdried timber as their raw material whenever possible, but we do not know the extent of the seasoning.

Until quite recently, all tree felling was done by axe. Many men could do fine work with this tool, as could the Laileys. A suitable tree having been felled, it seems more than likely that the trunk was chopped into billets, split, and the half rounds trimmed into cones (not hemispheres in the Bucklebury manner). These would be left stacked *in situ* for a year maybe. The drying process would be greatly accelerated by the reduction of unwanted timber. Being then in their lightest and most easily transportable form, they would be collected by packhorse with panniers or nets.

As the recovered cores show, the early bowl-turners machined to waste the entire interior wood from their bowls. At some unknown date, one such craftsman discovered that by making his turning tools or irons in a certain manner he could remove the interior of a bowl and use it to make a smaller one. Lailey (who thought that this procedure was unique to the Lailey family) advanced the idea that this was done to promote a saving in timber. There was such a saving, but the real, and very large, advantage was the gain in available working time. The trimming of a half-round to a hemisphere for an 18in (45cm) diameter blank took about 50 minutes. This done, no further preparation was needed for the other four bowls which followed in descending size. The core removed from the turning of the largest bowl was a blank ready to be spiked to the mandrel for the outside of the next one. Figure 27(B) illustrates this action. The important point to note is that a correctly sharpened tool follows a natural curve. Whereas the outside profile of a bowl was generated by the turner's eye, the inside shape required no sight of it and was determined by the tool used. The process does not function with any wood softer than sycamore (that is, the ornamental sort used by Jordan) as the lack of resistance causes the hook end of the tool to wander. Since some of Lailey's tools had come down to him from his grandfather, who would have learnt his trade as a boy in the 18th century, we can safely say that the latest date when this method was adopted would have been in that period. Perhaps earlier turner's tools may yet be discovered. If there is among them a hook tool with a curved shank, this will be a sure sign that concentric bowls were already being turned.

In the newspaper article which accompanied the publication in 1937 of Figure 29, Jordan, the Wellington, Salop, turner is quoted as saying that the only pole lathe turners then remaining in work were those in Wales. Evidently, he had no knowledge of Lailey at Bucklebury, Berkshire. Likewise, Lailey at a slightly earlier period thought himself to be the only such turner and remarked that there were no other bowl-turners save only north country ones, 'who use poplar wood and turn the whole of the inside of the bowl away to waste'. (The author has found no actual record of poplar bowls). The methods and machines of both turners were exactly alike and both derived from predecessors working well back into the 18th century. Allowing for only two preceding generations in machine and method terms before coming to a common prototype, this takes us to the 17th century at least.

As these two lathes, with their heavy headstocks and substantial wrought iron centres (pivots), are clearly the established pattern for bowl-turning work, it comes as no surprise to find evidence of a lathe for such craftsmen in the middle 13th century which is schematically the same. Figure 19 illustrates a bowl-turner at work, *c* 1250. As usual in representations of this sort, the artist has reduced and simplified what he saw. The lathe lacks a tool rest, and means of adjusting the tailstock. The entire machine is too fragile for the size of the bowl being turned. Nevertheless, in essence, this is Lailey's and Jordan's type of lathe. This lathe predates the bodger's form with its two moveable stocks, as also the Low Countries design with a slab bed (Figure 20). Lailey's and Jordan's lathes are the most likely pattern for the machines once used in the bowl-turners' workshops excavated at Coppergate, York, (rather than the portable woodland type currently exhibited at the Museum there).

Lailey always referred to his collection of mandrels (6) of various diameters as *mapers*. This term comes from the Old English *mapeltreow*, which means a maple (or sycamore) tree. The name of the commonest wood used to form these adjuncts had become, by transference, the name of the object itself. This is exactly equivalent to the use of the word *woods* for game bowls, despite their having been made from thermo-setting resin for a lifetime past. The head- and tailstocks were known as *puppets*. This is the country pronounciation of poppet, which really refers to the iron centres fitted to them. Here, the whole has become named from one of its parts. Similarly, the turner's tools were *irons*, an association akin to that of the *mapers*. There is some difficulty in determining the origin of the word lathe. The most likely guess is that it is related to the Old Norse *hlath*, which means a loom frame.

# NOTES on Chapter Three

1. References to Anglo-Saxon pottery and views here expressed are, in the main, derived from JG Hurst (1976) and Martin Millett (1990), but conclusions are the author's.

2. MU Jones has pointed out in correspondence that there is near certainty that a number of burials of ashes found in cemeteries in the west of England which have been interred without urns indicates the use of wooden bowls or pots for the purpose. These wooden pots have, of course, long since decayed away, but their traces have sometimes been detected.

3. Most of these data are derived from Morris (1984) by re-erecting figures from percentages to other bases given in her dissertation. Individual figures may thus be inexact, but not by large amounts. In recent correspondence, Dr Morris states that these figures have now been superseded, but that the relative quantities have not notably altered.

4. Allan, JP and Morris, CA 1984. These figures are from items W1 to W15.

5. Fitzrandolph, pp.56/7. Jordan would have been nearly 60 years old when the data for this work was collected. At this age, Lailey had already ceased to make very large bowls. In a timber yard, Jordan would have had ready access to extra labour for a double treadle, something denied to Lailey.

6. All Lailey's mandrels which have survived are at Reading, as Figure 27, save the largest. This is probably due to his not having turned anything over 12in (30cm) diameter during his later years, that is, since the last war. Both he and Jordan used much larger mandrels for heavy work, as may be seen in Figures 28 and 29. These look to be about 3in (7.5cm) in diameter. The lesser size of $2\frac{1}{2}$in (6.5cm) diameter has been adopted from trials on the actual Reading lathe which indicate that with anything much larger, the treadle stroke becomes too great and the driving belt fouls the mandrel on the upstroke. These trials were made by Godfrey Eke of the Reading Rural History Centre staff (now retired).

## Chapter Four

# The Economics of Bucklebury bowl turning

The economics of Lailey's trade in wooden bowls are best considered in reference to the inter-war period (1918-1939) as nearly all the available figures for price and output relate to that time. A fair estimate for his ladle-turning during the First War can be added. It is very doubtful whether Lailey ever received an order directly either from the Ministry of Munitions or from the Royal Mint. The ladles and bowls would have been ordered from an unidentified third party who would have issued instructions to Bucklebury, duly endorsed with the original contract number. Some far-seeing official from a Royal Ordnance Factory, and later the Royal Mint, who shopped at Harrods or another large store must have realised the possible uses of the wooden ladles and bowls. If it was Harrods which dealt with the ladles as middleman, these would have been passed on with the barest minimum handling charge as part of the store's war effort.

The known financial background to the period starts with the death of GW Lailey's father in 1912. There was then sufficient money in hand to build the roof of handmade tiles on the hut which was to last until 1959. It may be that there was too little for a really good job to be done on the cladding as well. In 1921, when he (GW Lailey) failed for whatever reason to buy the cottage on the manorial estate in which he lived, he was able to secure a plot nearby and have built the 'tin' bungalow in which he was to live for the next 25 years. About 1937, he was again with adequate funds to re-board the hut on the Common and to buy himself a plot of land in Briff Lane on which to build a new bungalow. From an economic standpoint, we know little of his (1939-1945) wartime activities, but we do know that he did eventually have built an excellent dwelling in brick in 1946 and that on his death in 1958 he had £1204 in the bank (1) in addition to owning a modern, freehold, brickbuilt bungalow, unmortgaged. In short, the Lailey business had been a profitable one for a long time.

All the figures which follow relate only to the 1918-1939 period. As the entire data are in Imperial measures and £.s.d. the text retains this form for clarity. Readers are referred to Table V which translates every amount so used in this and previous chapters into decimal coinage and metric measurements.

KS Woods, visiting Bucklebury in 1919, reported that the prices were from 3d to 3s. (2). These would have been for the standard range of bowls of 6in to 15in diameter, nominal and a knob. The word nominal is stressed because none of Lailey's bowls was made to an exact size, being adapted to the largest bowl which could be turned from a particular piece of timber. (Hers is the earliest report of the sunken-floor feature of the workshop. 'The turner works in a pit', she wrote).

His price list for the period reviewed was:-

| 6in | diameter bowl | | 6d |
|------|------|------|------|
| 9in | " | " | 1/6d |
| 12in | " | " | 2/-d |
| 15in | " | " | 3/-d |

The 3d mentioned was evidently for the core of the smallest bowl which he turned into a milliner's knob for hat stands. Even schoolboys were charged 6d for the 6in bowls. Thus, a set of bowls as above sold for total of 7/-d, or 7/3d with the knob. (These were sometimes made into whipping tops and sold for the same price to children).

Woods reported that these prices were considered low and HV Morton, writing in 1927, said so too. (His is the second written evidence for the pit in which lathe and turner stood. The third witness is the author in 1928). This probably enabled Lailey to weather the storm of falling prices in the late twenties. When prosperity returned in the thirties, he was able to raise them by about one third. There is evidence that demand at that time was greater than his ability to supply.

For the whole period under consideration, Lailey's elm wood came by lorry in ready cut half rounds. His earlier supplies, brought to the Common by pole wagon, would have been paid for on the basis of the Hoppus Measure for timber in the round, and bargained for by the load. He was now buying at the timber yard rate and this was 1/9d per cubic foot for cross-sawn elm, cut and delivered. But the volume was still worked out by the Hoppus formula and how this functioned is shown in Figure 31. For a set of bowls with a largest diameter of 15in, a billet of about 17in diameter was required and this, cut 17in long and split at the saw mill, yielded the blanks for two sets. Such a half round contained more than one cubic foot of wood (1930 cu in against 1728 cu in), but by Hoppus reckoning the charge was based on a little under threequarters of an actual cu ft (1296 cu in). The resultant material cost for each set of bowls from 15in diameter downwards was thus 1/3d for the four bowls, (6in, 9in, 12in, and 15in).

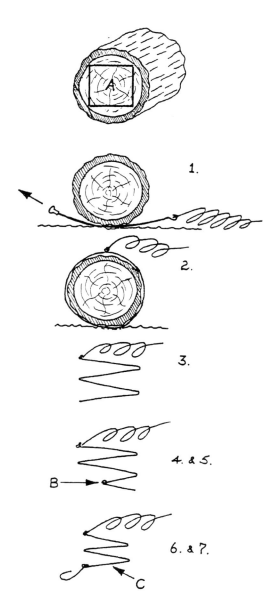

31. The Hoppus measurement system.

A tree having been felled, the quarter-girth measurement is used to determine the usable volume of timber therein. This is defined as the largest square section beam which can be cut from it and will be area A multiplied by the effective or actual length of the log.

1. Using a 'sword', which is a thin, flexible piece of iron with a hook end, a cord is passed under the log at the mid-point of its usable length.

2. The cord is knotted where it meets around the trunk.

3. It is folded in four.

4. One of the quarters is doubled again.

5. It is knotted again at B.

6. This leaves 7/8 of the original girth and this is re-folded into four.

7. The resultant hank is measured, at C.

8. This measurement is applied to the Hoppus Tables (original published in 1789) and the figure found is then multiplied by the usable length of the log. This gives the volume of a square beam of section A, and this is reckoned as the volume saleable and so charged for.

9. Nowadays, ready-corrected steel tapes are used. The principle is the same.

Allowing a cutting rate of 0.030in per revolution on all sizes of bowl, the floor-to-floor turning time can be calculated and produces the following approximate figures:-

| 15in | diameter bowl | 60 minutes |
|------|------|------|
| 12in | " | " | 25 " |
| 9in | " | " | 15 " |
| 6in | " | " | 10 " |

110 minutes

*Add*                              50 minutes for shaping the blank to a
                                   hemisphere
                                   160 minutes

or 2 hours 40 minutes for the set. During Lailey's normal working week of 6 days (54 hours in all) (3), 20 sets of 4 bowls each would have been produced. As all figures have been rounded upwards, he may have done somewhat better than this from time to time , but not by very much as an indeterminate time must be allowed for tool sharpening and for interruptions. (Many visitors noted his unwillingness to stop work and chat). The figure quoted by Woods of 12 dozen, or 144 bowls (that is 36 sets) a week must either be a mistake, or have been based on sets of three (12in, 9in and 6in) which he made when his timber was undersize. As she obtained the figure direct from Lailey, this is the probable answer to such a question as, 'How many bowls can you make in a week?' This figure comes very close to one based on the estimate above, taking the blank shaping time as 40 minutes, i.e. 90 minutes for a set of three bowls, (6in, 9in, and 12in).

The output estimated here would have returned some £7 a week gross, less £1 5s 0d for the material used, £5 15s 0d net. This was well over a craftsman's top rate of earning in an industrial town but equal to that of a senior foreman. (The current wage for first-class tradesmen in Reading at that time was 63/-d for a 48 hour week). If Lailey sold all the knobs as well (as stated in several contemporary accounts), his net takings came to £6, or a little more. Consignments of bowls for the London stores went by train from Thatcham station (GWR), carriage forward (4). They were packed in hessian sacks which were charged for. Local stores, such as Heelas at Reading, collected what they bought. Having dispensed with his pony and trap in the early twenties, Lailey had help from local traders with vans who delivered his sacks to the station at their convenience for a small fee.

At some time in the thirties, Lailey raised his prices, we do not know exactly by how much. He is recorded as having refused to accept 2/-d for an 8in (that is, a 9in under-sized) bowl c 1937. Presumably, he wanted the full 9in price which was, perhaps, 2/6 d by then. This increase would no doubt have been made in more than one step as it represents a rise of two thirds. Lailey would have been liable to pay Schedule A Income Tax (since abolished) on his 'tin' bungalow. This was based on its notional rental value, £50 a year, maybe. The basic rate was 5/-d in the £1. The Personal Allowance for a single man was £350 under Schedule D, so he might have been liable for some small amount under both Schedules combined. According to his own account (5), he was once visited at his workshop by someone from the Inland Revenue whom he persuaded that he was not liable for any tax. We have no date for this, but it was probably in the early thirties.

The price for the wartime (1914-18) ladles is thought to have been 9/-d each, which would have yielded perhaps £4 a week, high for those days. He may have continued to make them afterwards because they were his *tour de force*, and he liked to be seen working on one in photographs, as in Figure 32. It is also believed that he charged Harrods this same price for the 18in diameter bowls, three times the immediate post-war price for a 15in diameter bowl, and about right in terms of the time taken to make one. There is no source available for the price of the special 20in diameter bowls for the Royal Mint. This can hardly have been less than 15/-d and may even have been £1 each.

In 1930, for the first time since his mother's retirement, Lailey had an assistant, Edward Keene a retired Congregational Sunday-school superintendent, who lived nearby and had then turned eighty years of age, who helped him in two ways. He rough chipped the half-round billets, ready for their final reduction to a hemisphere, and he used a gouge to finish the inside of the bowl where the core had been broken out.

While the workpiece was still in the lathe, the turner applied sandpaper to the rim for a few strokes, to smooth it, and then pressed a block of carnauba wax to its surface. This gave it a polished yellow finish. A carpenter's pencil was then used for one more stroke to put a line round, just below the rim. (The wax and the pencil were kept in the bowl fixed to the top of the lathe headstock together with an oil bottle for lubrication of the centres as may be seen at the Reading Museum today). This

32. Lailey finishing a ladle, *c* 1920. He is in his early fifties. The handle of the ladle is being pared with a drawknife . The latest possible date for this picture is 1926 as by then he no longer wore a beard although he still had one in 1925. The earlier date is preferred as he did not continue making ladles for very long after the 1914-18 war. *Reading 35/4434.*

process, which commenced after 1918 when war work was over, was his only concession to any aesthetic notions. In a newspaper photograph of 1930, Keene is seen holding his gouge to the centre of a bowl, whilst Lailey is working on the underside of another with a drawknife to remove the centre pip left after parting off the waste. It is not known whether Keene also performed this task. Probably he did so. Whatever small remuneration he was given, we may be sure that it was recovered at a profit from additional turning output. Keene retired from the work after a few years (probably three) and Lailey was entirely alone in his workshop thereafter. After 1945, a great deal of Lailey's trade was in bowls for wedding gifts. His largest bowl was now 12in diameter and demand seems to have been for shallow forms. The required blank would thus have been much lighter than the hemispherical ones originally used. This would have reduced considerably the old man's labours (he had turned eighty in 1949) but it also meant his abandoning his cherished 'economy of timber' as the resultant cores would not form a blank for another bowl. This is clearly to be seen in the photograph which accompanied an article by R Beadington in *Country Life*, dated 20th March, 1958, where a selection of his current bowls is on view with the cores still undetached. (Appendix D has a description of Lailey turning a bowl).

Having supported himself and successive housekeepers for over forty five-years, and built two houses during that time, the craftsman's business cannot be said to have been unfruitful.

# TABLE V

| Conversion to decimal coinage of sums quoted in £ s.d. | |
|---|---|
| 1d | 0.417p |
| $1\frac{1}{2}$d | 0.625p |
| $1\frac{3}{4}$d | 0.729p |
| 3d | 1.25p |
| $3\frac{1}{2}$d | 1.458p |
| 6d | 2.50 p |
| 9d | 3.75p |
| 1/3d | 6.25p |
| 1/6d | 7.50p |
| 1/9d | 8.75p |
| 2/-d | 10.00p |
| 2/6d | 12.50p |
| 3/-d | 15.00p |
| 3s 6d | 17.50p |
| 5/-d | 25.00p |
| 6/-d | 30.00p |
| 7/-d | 35.00p |
| 7/3d | 36.25p |
| 9/-d | 45.00p |
| 12/-d | 60.00p |
| 63/-d | £3.15p |
| £1 5s 0d | £1.25p |
| £5 15s 0d | £5.75p |

| Conversion of Imperial measure to metric usage | |
|---|---|
| 0.30in | 0.8mm |
| 3in | 7.6cm |
| 6in | 15.2cm |
| 8in | 20.3cm |
| 9in | 22.9cm |
| 12in | 30.5cm |
| 15in | 38.1cm |
| 17in | 43.2cm |
| 18in | 45.7cm |
| 20in | 50.8cm |
| 24in | 61.0cm |

1 cu ft (1728 cu in) 0.0283 m$^3$.

# NOTES on Chapter Four

1. Private correspondence with Mrs Meg Cooper and his probated Will on file at Somerset House.

2. Woods, p.113. Katherine Woods was unwittingly responsible for starting one of several Lailey myths. (Appendix C).

3. This assumes a working week of 48 hours in winter and 60 hours in summer, effective working time. Actual time spent at the workshop would have been somewhat longer.

4. From author's conversations over the past 6 or 7 years with various people who had known the bowl turner, several of whom have since died, plus his own contact as a schoolboy in the late twenties, and correspondence with Mrs J. Wynne-Thomas, FSA who knew him from 1945.

5. The Times, 6/6/61.

*Chapter 5*

# The Reading Lathe in perspective

This study has confined itself to wooden bowls as essentially domestic utensils: mazers, loving cups and similar highly ornamented vessels are a large and separate subject (1). However, we note here that before *c* 1500 the word *mazer* meant only a drinking cup or goblet and that these, together with bowls and platters, were the normal products of the pole lathe turners.

Morris, in her Cambridge dissertation (1984), details some formidable examples of turners' output during the Middle Ages: 'many thousands' of wooden cups and dishes were supplied for Richard the Lionheart's coronation banquet (1189); in a single year (1248 ), a manor re-stocked its domestic stores with 2,350 platters and bowls; for Edward the First's wedding to Eleanor of Castille (1254), no less than 400 cups and 1,500 dishes were ordered.

The scene in the Bayeux Tapestry where Bishop Odo is blessing the food for the Duke and his guests (1066) shows what are clearly turned wooden bowls, platters and drinking cups and these must have been the normal tableware of the time. This emphasizes the point made in Chapter Three that an ample supply of turned wooden ware was one reason why the Anglo-Saxon immigrants were so slow in developing a potting industry. From the *adventus Saxonum* and hand moulding to the slow wheel was about 200 years; from the slow wheel to the fast one was another 200 years. That the migrants possessed excellent skills in wood turning is evidenced by the size of the bowls indicated by the recovered fragments which come both from England and from their continental homelands, some being noted in Chapter Three.

As mentioned in Chapter Two, HV Morton, visiting Lailey at work in 1927, strongly felt the Anglo-Saxon aura of what he saw. Little though he understood the turning process he was witnessing, he was surely right. Except that the turner's tools were tipped with a high carbon steel, unavailable before modern times, and that the turning of nested bowls belongs to later centuries, Lailey's procedures must have been exactly those of a bowl turner from the 5th century. Additionally, Morton noted that he 'stepped down into the workshop'. By this date, wood chippings and shavings had not yet filled the central part of this area though banks of them surrounded the working space. Besides carrying on a 5th/6th century trade and using virtually the same equipment (save only for the better tool steel), the turner also occupied a sunken-floored workshop exactly as his predecessors would have done in the Migration Period itself.

Unlike the chair bodgers, working in the Chiltern woods and remote from any power source, from *c* 1937 electric power was available on Turner's Green as Figure 33 shows. If Lailey had been asked why, with funds in the bank, he did not equip himself with a modern power-driven lathe at the time when he re-clad his workshop, he would doubtless have replied in the same terms as when he rejected the use of Col Julyan's 'Hand Made' steel stamp: that his customers preferred things as they were (2).

The Reading lathe was thus for 100 years the means of producing hand turned wooden bowls and ladles on a commercial basis and only for its last 30 years of active life was it becoming a museum piece. So we can say that workaday objects such as bowls, platters and cups have been made in wood in England for some fifteen centuries on pole lathes of which this one is the ultimate example. George William Lailey, its owner, who now rests close to Turner's Green (Figure 34) was the last bowl turner in England who used a pole lathe and followed his calling as a trade.

Nicholas Higham writes in his recent book about the Anglo-Saxons (3):

'Does it really matter what happened so long ago? Surely it does, and not just because of its curiosity value'.

He goes on to point out that the answer to such questions underlies what we are now and what are our modes of thought and that these things are relevant beyond these islands.

The Dark Ages, that is the first two centuries of the English nation, lack documentary indigenous records of any sort, our forbears being illiterate. Continental references are sparse and have to be very carefully interpreted. Within the Romano-British rump, we have the sermon of Gildas who wrote (*c* 550, perhaps) from a moralistic viewpoint. Many of his statements are demonstrably wrong. His view eastward from somewhere in the west country saw the Saxons as unmentionable barbarians who had steadily encroached upon the lands of Britain. Writing in Latin in the middle of the 6th century, what he says tells us almost nothing about the Angles, the Saxons and the Jutes, and eastern England as a whole.

The coming of Christianity (597) reintroduced literacy to England. Foremost among historical records is Bede's *Ecclesiastical History of the English Nation* (finished in 731). In it we do learn something of how people lived in those times. For real detail we must use the archaeological

33. The Bucklebury hut with electric power adjacent, from c 1937.
This photograph is heavily foreshortened. The electricity pole is over 100m away and the houses further still. This picture was taken in 1959. *Reading 5/432.*

record. On the grand scale, this gives us the Sutton Hoo ship burial and the Taplow princely burial. These are monuments to Top People and tell us little of how the common sort lived. For that, we have the excavated remains of their villages and hamlets, such as Mucking (4) and West Heslerton which belong to the earliest Pagan Period, and Wharram Percy where there is continuity of a sort from Roman times, and of course West Stow. From them we can realize what the migrants built when they arrived (excluding West Stow where the reconstructions are sadly misconceived).

From these and other sites and their adjoining graveyards, come a wealth of artefacts, largely the products of the smith, the potter and the worker in bone, native or imported. Where wood was buried, it is recognizable only from a soil trace or from attached metal parts - nails in a ship's timbers, clips and rims for wooden cups.

In the large Anglo-Saxon villages of eastern England and in the Thames valley, must always have been a smith and his forge, a wood turner and his pole lathe, and in many, a weaver, supported by the general spinning of thread by the women, and a worker in leather, traces of whose products are even rarer than those of the wood turner. Pottery, already mentioned in Chapter Three, in the form of Ipswich Ware (*c* 650) must have been the earliest craft centre established in England, that is, a product was made in the one place or area and distributed elsewhere.

In terms of how the people lived in those days (as opposed to their named but unknown rulers), we must look at the many trades from charcoal burning and hurdle making to rake making and bowl turning which have finally disappeared within modern times and which must have existed in 5th and 6th century England. These form connecting threads between today and yesterday and the Migration Period and collectively provide one facet of the answer to Higham's question. One of these threads terminates in the still workable machine on view at Reading today.

34. The grave of the last English bowl turner.
It lies within half a mile of his hut on Bucklebury Common. *Photograph by the author.*

# NOTES on Chapter Five

1. Mazers, post *c* 1500 became magnificent vessels, often turned in rare woods and adorned with carving by artists. Surviving examples are usually to be found in museums. Pinto, who is our authority on treen (or wooden plates and vessels generally) considers that mazers were turned on great-wheel lathes. Much harder woods such as hornbeam (and even lignum vitae) were employed. This must surely indicate an improvement of some sort in steel-making for the tipped tools employed. In the author's view, great-wheel lathes would have been excellent for finishing the cups, prior to carving, etc. but not solid enough for the rough turning which would have been done on lathes like the Dutch one in Figure 20.

2. The situation is analogous to that of the owners of articles in Sheffield silver plate. On many of those surviving, cleaning over 100 years or so has revealed traces of the underlying copper on the high points. There is a temptation to have the object re-plated by electro-deposition. Such an action would at once destroy its value as it would no longer be Sheffield plate.

3. Higham, 1993

4. Dixon, PH, 1993

# Appendix A

One of the many Lailey myths is to be found repeated in various writers from the mid-thirties onwards. Its general form is:

'Lailey lived in a folk-lore house on the Common, constructed by himself'.

At that time, and until 1946, he lived in the 'tin' bungalow in Long Grove, a mile or so from the Common. We also know for certain that all his skills were in the making of bowls and ladles of elm on a pole lathe, and that he did not have the capability to build a house. He may have helped with the 'tin' bungalow: he certainly did not erect it.

The above tale originated in *Bucklebury, a Berkshire Parish*, by A.L. Humphreys, Reading, 1932.

The opening and closing lines of Humphreys' account of Lailey's activities were printed thus (at the *heads* of pp. 371 and 373):

The Bowl-Turner - an old Berkshire craft. The following letter appeared in the 'Times' of March 18, 1924.                    Folk-lore

All Mr. Lailey's life has been spent on the common, where he lives in a house constructed by himself.                    Folk-lore

Two points are obvious: 'Folk-lore', which appears at the head of a broad RH margin, is a section title.

Secondly, ordinary English such as, 'He built himself a house on Acacia Avenue', does not mean that he personally constructed it.

So Humphreys was responsible for starting two separate hares (one, inadvertently) which ran for many years, until the seventies, at least.

---

# Appendix B

As the figures in Table I show, there was a notable change from a majority of soft woods used for bowls before *c* 1000 to a majority of harder woods thereafter. On the assumption that the available materials had not substantially changed, pre-and post-1000, it seemed that the reason must lie in the quality of the tools available to the turners having improved between the 5th century and the 10th. However, when Dr G McDonnell of English Heritage, an authority on steels, was consulted upon the point, he disagreed. In his opinion, tool steels during the Anglo-Saxon period were superior to those in Norman times. To confirm this, he adduced his findings from his article in *World Archaeology*, 1989.

This study contains the results both of Tylecote (from many sites) and his own from Hamwic and Coppergate. All data are from knives (for reasons which he explains), and all are graded by the hardness of the cutting edges. Below is his Table of some 69 measurements. They exclude the York and Hamwic findings. The corresponding Rockwell values have been added as these are more familiar to many engineers.

*Table A*

*Mean and Standard Deviations of hardness of knife blades*

| Period | Number of Measurements | MEAN HARDNESS | | Standard Deviation | |
|---|---|---|---|---|---|
| | | HV | Rockwell C | HV | Rockwell C |
| 1. Romano-British | 18 | 270 | 26 | 131 | 11 |
| 2. 5th-10th cent. | 12 | 463 | 46/47 | 198 | 16 |
| 3. 11th/12th cent. | 14 | 373 | 38 | 189 | 15 |
| 4. 13th cent. on | 14 | 363 | 37 | 154 | 13 |
| 5. 14th cent. on | 11 | 343 | 35 | 147 | 12 |

On the strength of the mean hardness figures, Dr McDonnell suggests that there was a marked improvement in cutting steel from Roman to Anglo-Saxon times, the latter yielding a peak result; thereafter came a small deterioration in each period from Norman to modern times. This is contrary to the known change in bowl turning from softer to harder woods from Period 2 to Period 3, as shown in Table I, so we must examine in more detail what these figures signify.

Taking Period 2 in Table A and differentiating the Standard Deviation of 198 (which is very large) and using round numbers we have:

*Table B*

3 knives of 270 HV      26 Rockwell C
3 knives of 285 HV      28     "

*Note this gap*

3 knives of 630 HV      57     "
<u>3 knives of 670 HV</u>     59     "
12

These figures yield: Mean hardness 464 HV and
Standard Deviation 195.
This is very close to the published figures of 463 HV and 198 SD.

Now tools for bowl turning need not only to be sharp enough (and thus hard enough) to cut cleanly the wood of the bowl blank (which involves a shearing action) but also to withstand the percussive effect of their first encounter with the rotating work piece. Among the Coppergate remains examined by Dr Morris (1982) were a number of prepared blocks which had become wastrels due to flaws of one sort or another. These showed clearly the large flats on a cone-shaped piece left by axe work. The turners had not yet developed the fine shaping used by the Laileys (Figure 1). With soft wood such as alder, this perhaps did not matter. Any reasonably hard tool would perform quite well with any of the softer woods. To turn harder woods, the tools used had to be harder to resist the wear imposed by the increased shearing stress. But if the tool steel were too hard, the cutting edge would be liable to chip or fracture and be constantly in need of re-sharpening. In his Table 3, Dr McDonnell lists 64 tools from Hamwic and Coppergate. Six are of inferior iron, seven are of good steel undifferentiated; the remaining 51 are all of good steel welded to an iron base in various ways. These last could only be resharpened for a limited number of times before the cutting edge was gone.

The turning of roughed out blanks in a hard wood, as described by Dr Morris, imposes a maximum percussive effect upon the tool in the early stages of work. To deal with this requires the tool steel to be hard, but not too hard. The recommended hardness for wood turning tools laid down in the Westinghouse Manual (both 1930 and 1937), itself based on a century of experience, is 45-48 Rockwell C, which corresponds to 440-480 HV. This will give a tool with the important characteristic which Westinghouse defines as 'toughness'.

This required hardness is exactly the mean hardness value for the 12 tools in Period 2 listed in Table A. Unfortunately, as shown in Table B, the Standard Deviation from the mean figure admits no tools anywhere near this value. However, these are all knife edges and knives are hardly of much use as turning tools. (The lower hardness would be for trimming wattles or similar operations; the higher for slicing rawhide to make thongs or the like).

It happens that Dr McDonnell has analysed a certain woodworking tool (Coppergate No. 9439) and has published the details. It is a spoon bit, lacking its driving tang, is well made, and in form it has a sheath of hard steel over a core of softer iron. Its cutting edges have a hardness of 420 HV (43 Rockwell C). This is only a little below the optimum for a turning tool. However, it belongs in time to the 900s, that is, towards the end of our arbitrary period for the early bowl turners. Thus, it reinforces the idea advanced earlier that, from a bowl turning viewpoint, toolmaking improved between the time of the *adventus Saxonum* (*c* 420) and the Norman invasion. This improvement was in the ability of the blacksmith to control his hardening processes so that tools could with certainty be made other than of high hardness or low hardness, and nothing between.

# Appendix C

Another Lailey myth was unwittingly started by Katherine Woods when she visited Lailey in 1919 in pursuit of information for her book, *Rural Industry round Oxford*, published 1921.

From her conversation with Lailey, she inferred that he had been exempted from the war-time call-up on account of his work for munition factories. Lailey himself fostered this myth in conversation with other visitors from this time on.

The second Military Service Act of 1916 passed into law in May of that year and raised the upper age for call-up to 41 years. But Lailey was already 48 years of age and thus exempt in any case. In the patriotic atmosphere of the day, which had resulted in many who were both under and over age volunteering for service in 1914 and succeeding years, one supposes that he felt it politic not to plead age but to claim that his war-work exempted him from service. In fact, his wooden ladles saved the country about 250 lbs (115 kg) approximately of copper (enough for about 1000 driving bands for 4in shells), plus about 400 hours of skilled working time. So he emphasized that he had 'done his bit'. There is also the fact that he did not 'look his age' at that time. When the author first saw him in 1928, he was about 60 years old, but his appearance was that of a man 10 to 15 years younger.

---

# Appendix D

Lailey's turning action.

Watching Lailey turn an elm bowl of modest size, one was struck by the way that he leaned forward, right over his work, at each stroke. (Something similar may be seen when certain people ride a bicycle uphill, especially a single-geared machine, leaning forward at each stroke as they pump along). This led one reporter to say, 'The work is very hard. The whole weight of the body is used to thrust the tool forward'. The reality was this: the forward action brought the body's weight as much as possible directly to bear on the treadle; this assisted the turning of the larger bowls, where the inertia to be overcome at each stroke was great. Turning nesting sets of four, three-quarters or more of the total turning time (and thus effort) was expended on the larger bowls. Having developed this action for the larger part of his turning time, he did not alter it when turning the smaller diameters. An observer of Lailey turning, say, a 9in bowl was thus given an impression of an enormous output of energy.

# Bibliography

| | | |
|---|---|---|
| Allan, JP and Morris CA | *Mediaeval and Post-Mediaeval Finds from Exeter - The Wooden Objects* | 1984 |
| Arnold, J | *The Shell Book of Country Crafts* | 1968 |
| Childe, GV | see Singer, Vol.I | 1954 |
| Cook, Jean | *Anglo-Saxon Buckets* | (forthcoming) |
| Davies, N de G | *Five Theban Tombs* | 1913 |
| Dixon, PH | *The Anglo-Saxon Settlement at Mucking: an interpretation* ASSAH No.6, Oxford | 1993 |
| Edlin HL | *Woodland Crafts in Britain* | 1949 |
| Fitzrandolph, HE | *The Rural Industries of England and Wales*, Vol.I | 1926 |
| Grimes, WF | *Excavation of Roman and Mediaeval London* | 1968 |
| Hall, R | *The Viking Dig* | 1984 |
| Haarnagel, W | *Die Grabung Feddersen Wierde* | 1979 |
| Higham, N | *Rome, Britain and the Anglo-Saxons* | 1993 |
| Humphries, AL | *Bucklebury, A Berkshire Parish* | 1932 |
| Hurst, JG | see Wilson, DM | 1976 |
| Jenkins, JG | *Traditional Country Craftsmen* | 1965 |
| Julyan, WL | *The Last of the English Bowl-turners* (unpublished) | 1939 |
| Lucas, A | *Ancient Egyptian Materials and Industries* | 1962 |
| Mcdonnell, G | *Iron and its alloys in fifth to eleventh centuries AD in England* World Archaeology, Vol.20 No.3 | 1989 |
| Manuelian, P der | *Notes on the So-called Turned Stools of the New Kingdom* (Museum of Fine Arts, Boston, Studies) | 1980 |
| Millet, M | *The Romanization of Britain* | 1990 |
| Millson, C | *Tales of Old Berkshire* | 1977 |
| Morris, CA | *Saxon and Mediaeval Woodworking Crafts* (unpublished Cambridge thesis) | 1984 |
| Morris, CA | *Pole Lathe Turning,* in Woodworking Crafts No.16 | 1985 |
| Morris, CA | *Aspects of Anglo-Saxon and Anglo-Scandinavian Lathe Turning,* in Woodworking Techniques, ed. S Mc Grail BAR Int. No 129 | 1982 |
| Morton, HV | *In Search of England* | 1927 |

| | | |
|---|---|---|
| Myres, JNL and Dixon, PH | A Nineteenth Century Grubenhaus *The Antiquaries Journal, Vol.XLVIII, Part 1* | 1988 |
| Oakley, KP | *Man the Toolmaker* | 1949 |
| Pinto, EH | *Treen* *Treen and Other Bygones* | 1949 1969 |
| Singer, C *et al.* | *A History of Technology, Vol.I* *Vol.II* | 1954 1956 |
| Wainwright, GA | Turnery from Kom Washim *Annales du Service des Antiquités de l'Egypte Tome XXV* | 1925 |
| Wilson, DM ed. | *The Archaeology of Anglo-Saxon England* | 1976 |
| Woods, Katherine S | *Rural Industries round Oxford* | 1921 |

# Ephemera

| | |
|---|---|
| The Times | 18. 3.24 |
| The Douai Magazine | Spring, 1927  Vol.IV No.3. |
| Newbury Herald and Berks County Paper | 29. 3.30 |
| Wellington Journal and Shrewsbury News | 8. 5.37 |
| Country Life | 28.12.45 |
| Country Life | 20. 3.58 |
| Newbury District News | 18.12.58 |
| The Times | 6. 6.61 |

# Conversations and correspondence

| | |
|---|---|
| Cooper, | Mrs Meg |
| Cripps, | Mrs Dorothy |
| Fitchett, | Alfred |
| Jones, | Mrs Margaret U |
| Millson, | Mrs Cecilia |
| Morris, | Dr Carole A |
| Richardson, | Dom Robert, OSB |
| Swinhoe, | Dom Bernard, OSB |
| Whitehouse, | Dr Helen |
| Wynne-Thomas, | Mrs Joan, FSA |